Field Studies, **9**, (1997) 1 - 177

A KEY TO THE MAJOR GROUPS OF BRITISH MARINE INVERTEBRATES

J. H. CROTHERS

Field Studies Council at Nettlecombe Court
Williton, Taunton, Somerset TA4 4HT

ABSTRACT

Keys are provided to the most of the Orders of invertebrate animals that have free-living representatives, over about 2mm in length, in marine habitats around the British Isles. The summary classification, and confirmatory notes, support the keys and include parasitic and microscopic groups. References are provided for further identification to family, genus and species.

CONTENTS

INTRODUCTION

The range of animal life to be found in our marine habitats is much greater than that seen anywhere else in Britain. There are not necessarily any more individuals, or any more species, present but the community is made up from a wider range of animal types. A five minutes plankton haul, a walk on the shore at extreme low water, or (better still) a brief dive into the sublittoral, can reveal whole new worlds of animal life, unimagined by the land-based naturalist. Frequently, it is not just the genus and species which are unknown; the Phylum and the Class pose problems as well.

Fortunately, there is a wealth of published information available to help us identify British marine invertebrates – but, all too often, the books and papers fall into one of two categories. One deals, in a general way, with the whole fauna whilst the other considers a few selected groups in great detail. The problem, in both cases, lies in deciding whether, or not, a particular specimen is included in the book. This is the problem which renders marine invertebrates a 'difficult group' and justifies the inclusion of the present guide within the AIDGAP Project.

Although planned to be uniform with the other *Keys to Major Groups of British Invertebrates* (Croft, 1986: Tilling, 1987), this work is more complicated, not least because it is harder to define precisely what is meant by 'British'. The key should apply to animals found from high water mark around the British Isles, out to the 200m depth contour. Inhabitants of the intertidal zone are, of necessity, transitional between marine and terrestrial or freshwater faunas. This key includes such transitional forms, with the exception of flying insects, almost all of which *might* be blown onto the shore at some time. As before, the term 'Major Groups' means Phyla, Classes, and Orders, with occasional descent to Suborders or Superfamilies. 'Animals' is used in the sense of Margulis & Schwartz (1982) so excludes members of the unicellular Kingdom Protoctista.

British terrestrial invertebrates (Tilling, 1987) were described in terms of 36 Orders, belonging to 13 Classes and 7 Phyla. British freshwater invertebrates (Croft, 1986) were comparable, requiring 31 Orders in 10 Classes and 10 Phyla. In contrast, and despite the fact that our marine fauna, in terms of species, numbers between a third and a quarter of our terrestrial one, this work involves 204 Orders in 64 Classes and 33 Phyla (one of which was first described after the original version had been tested!).

These keys were originally planned to enable a field biologist to identify (to Order) any marine invertebrate found in British waters. A Test Version was evaluated in 1994. I am very grateful for the time and detailed effort that many people must have spent. Many testers experienced problems of scale when using keys which included microscopic and macroscopic forms together – so in this, the first published, version the keys have been restricted to specimens more than about 2mm long.

The keys were also planned as an entry port for the *Synopses of the British Fauna*. Where no *Synopsis* was currently available, the reader would be directed towards another source. Usually, this is to one of four books, published during the long gestation of this work. Pearse, Pearse, Buchsbaum and Buchsbaum (1987) *Living Invertebrates* brings the wonder of *Animals without Backbones* to a new generation of biologists and provides an invaluable background text. Hayward & Ryland (1990) *The Marine Fauna of the British Isles and North-West Europe* is the finest single work on the subject – but sold at an astronomical price. Their, slightly abbreviated (1995), *Handbook of the Marine Fauna of North-West Europe* is much more reasonable. Hayward *et al.* (1996) Collins Pocket Guide *Seashore of Britain and Northern Europe* has beautiful colour plates.

Despite popular prejudice, taxonomy is a living science. Fresh information encourages reappraisal of the relationships within and between groups and there has never been a time when the academic world shared a common view on the detailed classification of marine invertebrates. Like other overviews, this takes a subjective line between incompatible taxonomies – and nobody is more aware than the author that the scheme presented here should be regarded as provisional.

The classification on which the keys are based is summarised in Appendix 1 (page 161). The number of British species in each group was compiled, where possible, from the texts recommended in the relevant Confirmatory Notes and, for molluscs, from Smith & Heppell (1991). In other cases, various British marine faunas were consulted, particularly Bruce, Colman and Jones (1963) and Marine Biological Association (1957). Where I was unable to establish a plausible figure, I have not made an entry. The final total is, consequently, an underestimate of the true British marine invertebrate fauna.

How to Use the Keys

When confronted with a totally unknown marine invertebrate, turn to the Pictorial Key on p.4. This directs you to either Key 2 of Key 3 which are laid out in couplets, following the traditional dichotomous (two-branched) convention. The first couplet of Key 2 asks you whether or not your specimen has articulated limbs. If the former is true, you continue at couplet 2:2 (in the latter case, you would turn on to couplet 2:3) and answer a second question. In many cases, sooner or later, you will be directed to another key which works in the same way. Frequently, there will be illustrations beside the couplet. It is unlikely that these illustrations will look exactly like your specimen because of the number of species involved and close attention should be paid to the text. Resist the temptation to attempt identification by flicking through the pictures, except in the pictorial key. The number following the couplet number shows where you have come from, just in case you need to retrace your steps!

The Illustrations are taken, where possible, from the *Synopsis* (or other work) recommended for subsequent identification to species in the confirmatory notes.

The Confirmatory Notes, which follow the keys, summarise the main features of each Major Group. They are more comprehensive than the keys and include parasitic groups. The original intention had been to deal solely with free-living marine invertebrates but the dividing lines between genuine independent livelihoods, commensalism and parasitism are so vague (and often invisible to a cursory glance) that I have adopted a pragmatic approach in the keys supported by rather fuller confirmatory notes. In compiling them (and hence the keys), I relied heavily on other people's work. Wherever possible, I worked from the relevant volumes of the *Synopses* available to me in 1996. For many of the other groups, Hayward and Ryland (1990; 1995) were very useful. Smith & Heppell (1991) was valuable for molluscan classification. Much of my information on planktonic forms has come from the *Fiches d'identification du Zooplancton*. All the works consulted are listed in the references. The whole required a unified scheme of classification and, here, I relied upon Barnes (1984) and Pearse, Pearse, Buchsbaum & Buchsbaum (1987). No one text has been followed slavishly and responsibility for all the resulting errors is mine alone.

Scale. The testing phase revealed many problems associated with size of the specimen. Although there is a finite maximum size that can be attained by any organism, all must start small. Thus, crabs which can exceed 300mm across the carapace first appear at 2mm. As with Croft (1986), the present version of this key does not attempt to identify specimens smaller than 2mm.

The Glossary (p.144) decodes the very many technical terms used in this guide. **Bold type** is used in the text (at their first appearance) to identify those terms which are included in the glossary.

Scope. The key was written for a field biologist with occasional access to a binocular microscope. The assumption is made that the specimen is alive, more than 2mm long and is being viewed under sea water – unless some comment is made to the contrary.

Many marine invertebrates live as discrete, recognisable individuals, e.g., a crab. Others are clearly colonial (e.g., a sea mat) but almost every possible intermediate condition can be found. Amongst the colonial forms, the component 'individuals' – variously called polyps or zooids according to their phylum – are often tiny, but the colony may be large. Individuals may behave independently of each other or may co-operate so that the colony acts as a 'super-individual'. Therefore, this key starts off using the term 'specimen' (rather than 'animal') to denote the subject to be identified, only uses 'animal' or 'colony' once the true nature of the beast has been established.

Choose one of the two
descriptions below

1. The specimen is able to move about (from one place to another) on its own by floating, by swimming, by walking, by crawling, by gliding, by burrowing or by some other means.

GO TO KEY 2
opposite

2. The specimen is unable to move about on its own, remaining attached to, or living within, a firm substratum. That substratum may move or it may stay in one place. It may be inanimate (a rock or the hull of a ship) or be the body of another, perhaps mobile, marine organism.

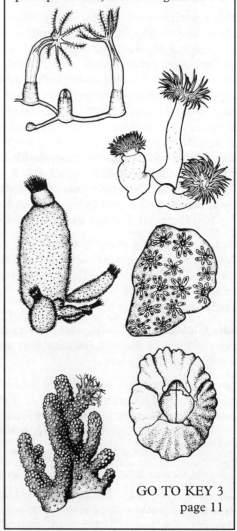

GO TO KEY 3
page 11

KEY 2

A KEY TO MOBILE ANIMALS

All the keys were written for field biologists with, on occasion, limited laboratory support such as binocular microscopes, and the assumption is made that the specimen is alive, and is being viewed under sea water, unless some comment is made to the contrary. **Bold type** in the text indicates terms that are defined in the glossary (p. 144).

2:1   – The specimen has articulated limbs (arms, legs[1] or antennae), clearly divided into **segments**[2], which it uses for locomotion (e.g. Figs 401-407, 501) **2:2**

–   The specimen is without 'arms' or 'legs' or, if such **appendages** *are* present, they are not broken up into a series of segments **2:3**

2:2   (2:1) – The specimen is **radially symmetrical**, and without a distinct head. 5 - 12 (typically 5 or 10) **arms** are attached, equidistantly, around a central disc. (Fig. 201) ....**Key 4:3** (p. 14)

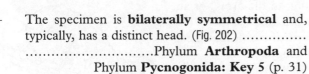

Fig. 201

–   The specimen is **bilaterally symmetrical** and, typically, has a distinct head. (Fig. 202) ....
...............................Phylum **Arthropoda** and Phylum **Pycnogonida: Key 5** (p. 31)

Fig. 202

---

[1] A very small (not thought to be more than 1.2mm long) squat animal which walks with a lumbering gait on 4 pairs of stubby, unjointed legs might cause confusion. Living amongst barnacles and mussels, or **interstitially** between sand grains. Water bear, Sub-Phylum **Tardigrada** (p.136).

[2] Segment. There is a confusion of terminology in the literature. Some authors use the word 'segment' for the body somites of, for example, a worm or a shrimp. Others use it for the sections of arthropod appendages. I have tried to follow the latter convention and use 'somite' for the replicated sections of the body.

2:3   (2:1) – The body **somites** are clearly visible. On
        closer examination, any 'legs' are seen to be
        stumpy outgrowths of the body, **parapodia** (one
        on each side of most somites), each bearing a tuft
        of bristles (**chaetae**). The animal rows itself
        through the water, sand or mud. (Fig. 203). Annelid
        worm ....**Key** 7 (p. 65)

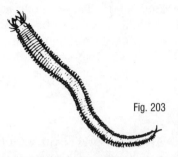

Fig. 203

  –   No body somites can be seen **2.4**

2:4   (2:3) – The specimen has conspicuous large eyes.
        It 'swims' by jet propulsion but, if crawling, uses 8,
        suckered, arms that grow out from the head. (Fig.
        204, Fig. 205 and Fig. 206). Capable of rapid colour /
        pattern changes when alive ....
        ...Phylum **Mollusca** Class **Cephalopoda** **2:5**

  –   Eyes, if present, are not large and conspicuous; the
        specimen does not swim by jet propulsion and
        does not have 8 arms, bearing suckers, growing
        out from the head **2:7**

2:5   (2:4) – The animal has 2 tentacles (on which the
        suckers are clustered into a 'club' at the distal end)
        in addition to the 8 arms, which bear suckers
        along their whole length. The streamlined body
        bears fins along each side and may contain an
        internal shell **2:6**

  –   Without tentacles (in addition to the arms) or an
        internal shell. Any fins on the globular body are
        small and rounded. If present, these do not meet
        at the hind end. (Fig. 204). Octopus
        ....Order **Octopoda** (p.117)

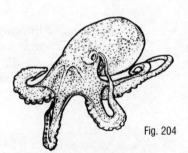

Fig. 204

2:6 (2:5) – The two long tentacles (much longer than the arms) can be retracted into pits. The lateral fins do not (quite) meet at the rear end of the body. (Fig. 205). Cuttlefish or little cuttle............
......................................Order **Sepioida** (p. 117)

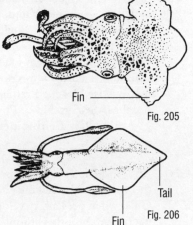

Fin

Fig. 205

– The two tentacles are not much longer than the other 8 arms, and cannot be retracted into pits. The lateral fins meet at the rear end of the body, which may be extended into a long 'tail'. (Fig. 206). Squid ....Order **Teuthoida** (p. 117)

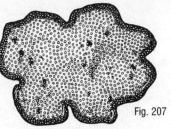

Tail

Fin Fig. 206

2:7 (2:4) – The specimen lives within, or bears on its back, an **external** calcareous **shell** composed of between 1 and 8 plates (**valves**). There is no internal skeleton ....**Key 6** (p. 46)

– The specimen does not live within, nor carry on its back, an external shell composed of discrete plates, although it may be covered with calcareous spines. There may be an internal hard skeleton
....**2:8**

Are you looking through a hand lens or microscope?

2:8 (2:7) – A very small specimen (< 3mm diameter), like a giant *Amoeba*. Lacking any symmetry. It is without a head, limbs or organs. The archetypal 'found in the lab' animal, only known from marine aquaria. (Fig. 207) *Trichoplax adhaerens*
..............................Phylum **Placozoa** (p. 79)

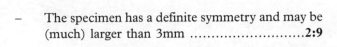

Fig. 207

– The specimen has a definite symmetry and may be (much) larger than 3mm **2:9**

2:9 (2:8) – The body surface of the specimen is hidden beneath spines, spicules or scales **2:10**

– The body surface of the specimen is not covered in spines, spicules or scales **2:12**

2:10 (2:9) – The specimen's body is shaped like that of a worm – an elongated cylinder. There is no internal skeleton ......Phylum **Mollusca** **2:11**

– The body is not worm-like but distinctly globular. There is a hard calcareous internal skeleton (or test) whose bleached remains may be stranded on beaches. Sea urchin ...Phylum **Echinodermata** Class **Echinoidea** ......**Key 4:10** (p. 16)

2:11 (2:10)[3] – Body with a conspicuous furrow down the ventral side, linking the mouth and the anus. Gills, when present, developed as folds and not bi-pectinate. Mouth without a foot-shield. (Fig. 208) ....Class **Solenogastres** (p. 107)

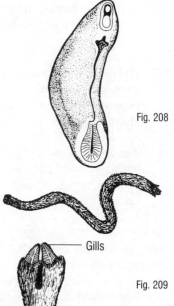

Fig. 208

– Body without a ventral furrow. and with a pair of bi-pectinate gills emerging from the anal cavity at the posterior end. Mouth surrounded by a foot shield. (Fig. 209) ......Class **Caudofoveata** (p. 107)

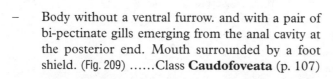

Gills

Fig. 209

2:12 (2:9)– The specimen is **radially symmetrical**, or nearly so, and is without a head ......**Key 4** (p.14)

– The specimen is **bilaterally symmetrical**, and may have a distinct head **2:13**

2:13 (2:12) – On the underside of the body, the specimen has a flattened, typically muscular but sometimes ciliated, surface on which it crawls (called the foot) **2:14**

– Specimen apparently without a foot **2:18**

---

[3] If neither of these alternatives seems appropriate, proceed to Key 7, p. 65.

2:14 (2:13) – A small (typically less than 20mm) *very flat* specimen which glides over the substratum. The body does not necessarily change shape whilst moving. The sides of the body sweep down to touch the substratum without any intervening ridge. Upper (**dorsal**) surface generally smooth. The common mouth / anus is positioned on the lower (**ventral**) side. No gills. (Fig. 211 and Fig. 212).
Flatworm ....Phylum **Platyhelminthes**
............................Class **Turbellaria** **2:15**

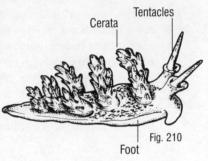

Cerata   Tentacles

Fig. 210

Foot

– A slug or slug-like animal, often with a conspicuous ridge along the side of the body overhanging the edge of the foot as might the eaves of a bungalow. Crawls over the substratum by muscular contractions of the foot musculature. Dorsal surface smooth or variously decorated with tubercles or extensive growths (**cerata**). Typically with an obvious head, bearing a mouth and paired tentacles. Sometimes with conspicuous gills near the posterior end, generally surrounding the anus. (Fig. 210) ....Phylum **Mollusca**
............................Class **Gastropoda** 2:16

2:15 (2:14) – A high intertidal flatworm, much longer (*ca* 6x) than broad, with a single pair of eyes. Front of the head rounded, or (in *Procerodes* Fig. 211) with stubby **marginal tentacles** (like ears) but never with **nuchal tentacles** arising from the upper surface. Up to 11mm in length ....
..............................Order **Tricladida** (p. 90)

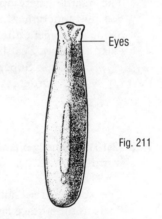

— Eyes

Fig. 211

– A lower shore or subtidal flatworm, not more than 4x longer than broad, with many eyes, typically arranged in clusters. Front of the head rounded, perhaps with two marginal tentacles: with, or without, nuchal tentacles arising from the upper surface. Up to 40mm in length. (Fig. 212) ....
..............................Order **Polycladida** (p. 90)

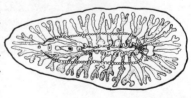

Fig. 212

2:16 (2:14) – The specimen has an internal shell whose position may be seen from the dorsal side, or felt when gently compressed with a finger ....
....**Key 6** (p. 46)

– The specimen does not have an internal shell ......
....**2:17**

2:17 (2:16) – A slug, up to about 10mm long, with a single pair of short, retractile, **head tentacles** bearing eyes at their tips. **Mantle** dark grey, and covered with tubercles, contrasting with the pale grey foot. Air-breathing, with the opening to the **mantle cavity** high up on the posterior end, just beneath the 'eaves' of the mantle. Silhouette toothed, when viewed from above. *Onchidella celtica*. (Fig. 213) ....Super-Order **Pulmonata** ....Order **Systelommatophora** (p. 113)

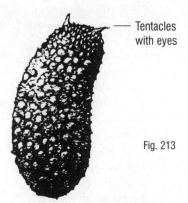

Tentacles with eyes

Fig. 213

– The head tentacles do not have eyes at their tips. The mantle cavity opens forwards (if at all) and does not function as a lung. (The animal breathes dissolved oxygen, often through dorsally-mounted gills.) (Fig. 214). Sea slug ....
.....................Super-Order **Opisthobranchia** Orders **Acochlidioidea** (p. 111) and **Nudibranchia** (p. 112)

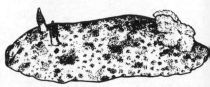

Fig. 214

2:18 (2:13) – The general shape of the specimen is worm-like ....**Key 7:4** (p. 66)

– The specimen is not in the least worm-like, it floats in the surface layers of the sea ....
....**Key 4: 39** (p. 26)

KEY 3

A KEY TO SESSILE (FIXED) ANIMALS

All the keys were written for field biologists with, on occasion, limited laboratory support in the way of binocular microscopes, and the assumption is made that the specimen is alive, and is being viewed under sea water, unless some comment is made to the contrary. **Bold type** in the text indicates terms that are defined in the glossary (p. 144).

3:1 – The specimen is **radially symmetrical**, or nearly so, and is without a distinct head ....
....**Key 4** (p. 14)

– The specimen is **bilaterally symmetrical** and may have a distinct head, or shows no particular symmetry **3:2**

3:2 (3:1) – The specimen lives within, or under, a protective, perhaps calcareous, shell, case or tube. Individuals are discrete – they may aggregate but are not joined together in a colony **3:3**

– Individuals do not live within or under their own calcareous shell, case or tube but, if they form a colony, there may be many 'individuals' (**polyps** or **zooids**) within a common outer 'skin' **3:6**

3:3 (3:2) – The specimen lives within a tube of its own making, perhaps cemented to the substratum (or to other tubes) along most of its length although the open end may rise up into the water (or air)
....Phylum **Annelida**
Class **Polychaeta** **3:4**

– The specimen lives within a shell ....
....**Key 6:8** (p. 48)

3:4 (3:3) – The worm lives in a white calcareous tube, perhaps coiled in a spiral (family Spirorbidae), perhaps winding across the rock surface (family Serpulidae). Fan worm (family Sabellidae). (Fig. 301) ....Order **Sabellida** (p. 105)

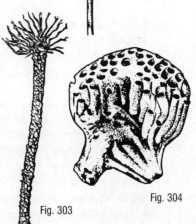

Fig. 301

–   The worm lives in a tube made from sand or mud grains **3:5**

3:5 (3:4) – The worm lives in a tube made of mud, sticking up out of a sandy, muddy or gravelly substratum. Fan worm (family Sabellidae) (Fig. 302) ....Order **Sabellida** (p. 105)

Fig. 302

–   The worm lives in a tube made of sand grains. Tubes may occur singly (Fig. 303) or may be clustered together in a massive reef (Fig. 304) ....Order **Terebellida** (p. 105)

Fig. 304

Fig. 303

3:6 (3:2) – Sooner or later, the specimen will extend tentacles into the water with which it attempts to feed. There may be a single large crown of tentacles or, if the specimen is actually a colony, there may be dozens, scores, hundreds or even thousands of crowns of small tentacles ....**Key 4** (p. 14)

–   The specimen is without tentacles. It is a filter feeder, straining material from water currents established within its body. Such currents are often apparent under the microscope **3:7**

3:7 (3:6) – The specimen appears to be solitary (an individual animal living on its own)...............**3:8**

– The specimen appears colonial (many 'individuals' living together and organically fused one to another) **3:9**

3:8 (3:7) – With two, 'conspicuous', **siphons** (inhalant and exhalant) (Fig. 305). When squeezed gently, the body produces a thin stream of water. Sea squirt ....Phylum **Chordata** Class **Ascidiacea** (p. 141)

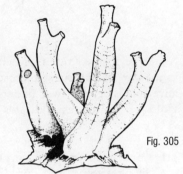

Fig. 305

– Specimen flask or bag shaped with a single (exhalant) siphon. Inhalant openings generally invisible. Does not squirt water when squeezed[4]. (Fig. 306). Purse sponge ...Phylum **Porifera** (p. 79)

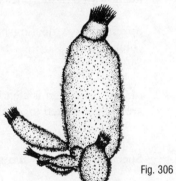

Fig. 306

3:9 (3:7) – Either, the zoids have paired **inhalant** and **exhalant siphons**, or they have individual inhalant siphons but discharge into a common exhalant **atrium**. In the latter case, the individual zoids are unrecognisable as such and the inhalant siphons are arranged in a rough star or oval around their atrium. (Fig. 307). Colonial sea squirt ....Phylum **Chordata** Class **Ascidiacea** (p. 141)

Inhalant siphons

Atrium

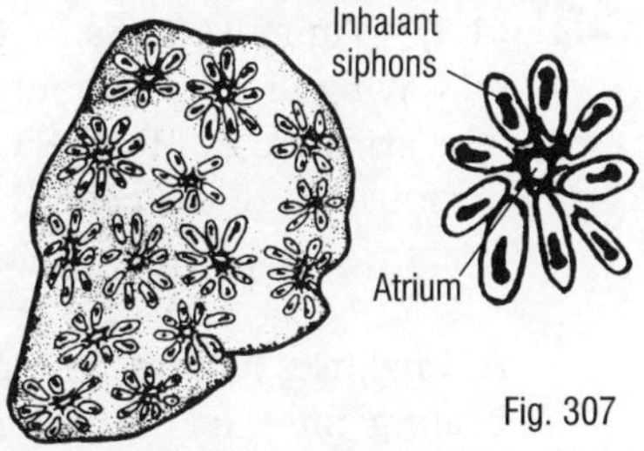

Fig. 307

– With a number of conspicuous exhalant openings scattered over the upper surface of the colony. Never paired. Inhalant openings generally invisible. (Fig. 308). Sponge ....Phylum **Porifera** (p. 79)

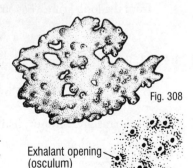

Fig. 308

Exhalant opening (osculum)

---

[4] If this does not seem an appropriate description, and your animal is worm-like in shape, consider Key 7 couplet 7:40 p.78.

KEY 4

A KEY TO ANIMALS WITH AN ESSENTIALLY RADIAL SYMMETRY

All the keys were written for field biologists with, on occasion, limited laboratory support in the way of binocular microscopes, and the assumption is made that the specimen is alive, and is being viewed under sea water, unless some comment is made to the contrary. **Bold type** in the text indicates terms that are defined in the glossary (p. 144).

4:1 – Specimen was living on the shore or sea bed, attached to a hard substratum or living within a soft one **4:2**

– Specimen was floating on the surface of the sea or swimming within the water column **4:37**

4:2 (4:1) – Specimen is clearly an individual animal with **"arms"** (Figs 401-407), which are not connected together with a web of skin (cf. Fig. 439) ....Phylum **Echinodermata** in part **4:3**

– Specimen without '**arms**' of this type **4:8**

4:3 (4:2) – Animal moves by gliding over the substratum, using its **tube feet**, and not by waving the arms about (although it may raise the leading arms up in the water). The arms are not feathery (cf. Fig. 406). If the animal has only 5 arms, it may not be obvious where the central **disc** ends and the **arms** begin. (Figs 401-403). Starfish ... .Class **Asteroidea** **4:4**

– Animal uses its arms in movement, either levering itself across the substratum or by beating them in the water to swim. The small central disc is clearly demarcated from the long arms. (Figs 405-407) **4:6**

4:4 (4.3) – There is a row of conspicuous, large plates along the edges of the arms. (Fig. 401) ....Order **Phanerozonida** (p. 139)

– The arms are without distinctive plates **4:5**

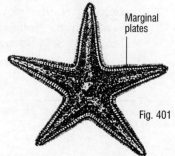

Marginal plates

Fig. 401

4:5 (4:4) – The skin over the **dorsal** (**aboral**) surface of the body bears spines but not tiny pincers (**pedicellariae** – hand lens needed cf. Fig. 403). May have more than 5 arms, as in Fig. 402............
..........................Order **Spinulosida** (p. 139)

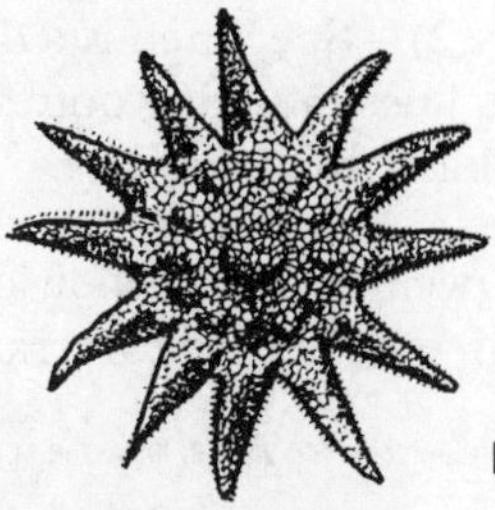

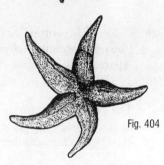

Fig. 402

– The skin over the **dorsal** (**aboral**) surface of the body bears tiny pincers (**pedicellariae**) but not spines (hand lens needed, Fig. 403). Never more than 5 arms. (Fig. 404) ....
........................Order **Forcipulatida** (p. 139)

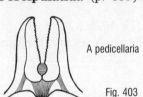

A pedicellaria

Fig. 403

Fig. 404

4:6 (4:3) – The 10 feathery arms can be used for swimming but not for crawling or holding on to the substratum. When the animal is attached, the mouth (and thus the whole mouth-bearing (**oral**) surface) faces upwards. (Fig. 405). Feather star ...
...Class **Crinoidea** Order **Comatulida** (p. 138)

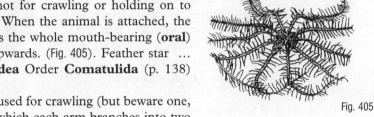

Fig. 405

– The 5 arms are used for crawling (but beware one, rare, species in which each arm branches into two close to the base – Fig. 406). The animal cannot swim. It is not attached to the substratum, and lives with its mouth bearing surface downwards. Brittle star ....Class **Ophiuroidea** **4:7**

4:7 (4.6) – The long coiled arms may be branched, as in Fig. 406 ....Order **Euryalae** (p. 139)

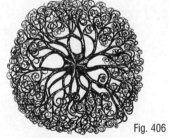

Fig. 406

– The arms are never branched and cannot be coiled. (Fig. 407) ....Order **Ophiurae** (p. 139)

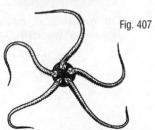

Fig. 407

4:8 (4.2) – Specimen is a discrete animal with 'tentacles' (actually **tube feet**) arranged in lines radiating outwards from the region of the mouth (**oral surface**) across, or along, the body **4:9**

– Specimen, or the individual **polyps** or **zooids** within a colony, either without tentacles or with tentacles arranged in one or more rings, horseshoes or spirals ...**4:14**

NOTE: If no tentacles are visible, leave the specimen undisturbed in seawater for 20 mins, to be sure

4:9 (4:8) – The animal's body is covered in spines. It has a rigid calcareous skeleton (the test) so cannot alter its shape – apart from moving its spines. Without tentacles (apart from the tube feet). Often globular in shape. (Figs 408-410). Sea urchin ....Class **Echinoidea** **4:10**

– The animal is approximately cylindrical in form, is without spines, is able to alter its body shape and to extend tentacles into the water from the anterior end. (Figs. 411-414). Sea cucumber ....Class **Holothuroidea** **4:12**

4:10 (4:9) – The conspicuous mouth (with obvious jaws, reminiscent of the closed chuck of a drill) is positioned centrally in the lower surface. The anus is in the centre of the upper (aboral) surface, and difficult to see. A truly radially-symmetrical animal, with no visible 'front end', living on hard substrata. (Fig. 408). Regular sea urchin ....
........................Order **Diadematoida** (p. 140)

Fig. 408

– The anus is not in the centre of the aboral surface. The animal shows some sign of (secondary) bilateral symmetry: there is a recognisable 'front end' (Figs 209-210). A burrowing sea urchin, found in sand and muddy sand **4:11**

4:11 (4:10) – The mouth and anus are close together on the same surface. (Fig. 409). Sea potato ....
........................Order **Clypeastroida** (p. 140)

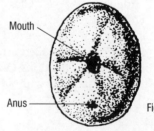

Mouth

Anus

Fig. 409

– The mouth and the anus are at the opposite ends of the test. (Fig. 410). Heart urchin ....
...........................Order **Spatangoida** (p. 140)

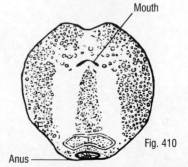

Mouth

Fig. 410

Anus

4:12 (4:9 or 4:32) – A worm-like animal with with no tube feet or respiratory trees; 11 or 12 tentacles, (Fig. 411).....................Order **Apodida** (p. 140)

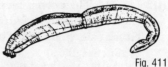

Fig. 411

– A sausage-shaped animal with definite rows of tube feet along the body (Figs 412-414); may have more than 12 tentacles (range 10-30) **4:13**

Fig. 412

4:13 (4:12) – Sea cucumber with between 15 and 30 shield-shaped tentacles. Only the lower (ventral) rows of tube feet are used to move around (Fig. 413) ....Order **Aspidochirotida** (p.140)

Fig. 413

– Sea cucumber with between 10 and 30 highly branched retractile tentacles. May use any or all the rows of tube feet when moving. (Fig. 414) ......
.....................Order **Dendrochirotida** (p. 140)

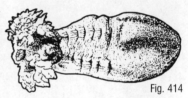

Fig. 414

4:14 (4:8) – The specimen is a colony composed of many 'individuals' (called **polyps** or **zooids** depending to which major group they belong) which have budded asexually from the founding individual, remaining in tissue contact with each other and living within a common skin or case.
....**4:15**

– The specimen is a solitary individual. These animals may have budded from a common parent, or may otherwise aggregate together, but they have neither maintained, nor subsequently established, tissue contact one with another **4:30**

4:15 (4:14) – The polyps have 8 tentacles, each bearing short side arms (**pinnae**) evenly spaced down either side (Fig. 415). The tentacles are arranged symmetrically in a single ring around the mouth ....Phylum **Cnidaria** Sub-Phylum **Anthozoa** Class **Octocorallia**......**4:16**

NOTE: all have 8 tentacles

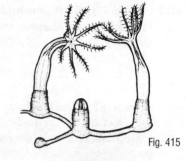

Fig. 415

–   The polyps or zooids which make up the colony have tentacles (usually more than 8) without **pinnae** (Fig. 416), although they may bear **cilia** **4:19**

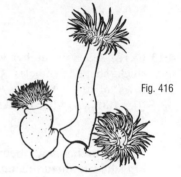

Fig. 416

4:16 (4:15) – A delicate, beautifully-structured colony, standing erect in the water **4:17**

–   The somewhat amorphous colony encrusts rocks, or forms erect, irregularly-lobed, fleshy masses... ....**4:18**

4:17 (4:16) – The colony forms an erect branching tree-like structure, attached to a hard substratum. (Fig. 417). Sea fan ......Order **Gorgonacea** (p.87)

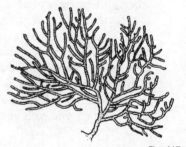

Fig. 417

–   The colony resembles a large feather, or a rye grass flower head, stuck shaft down into mud or sand. (Figs. 418). Sea pen ...Order **Pennatulacea** (p.87)

Fig. 419

4:18 (4:16) – The polyps arise singly from a narrow creeping tube (**stolon**). These stolons may form a complex encrusting network or even coalesce into a membranous sheet. (Fig. 419) ....
...............................Order **Stolonifera** (p.87)

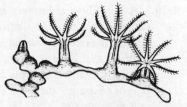

Fig. 419

– The colony forms a thick enveloping layer or an erect fleshy mass, perhaps reminiscent of podgy human fingers (Fig. 420). Soft coral ....
...............................Order **Alcyonacea** (p.87)

Fig. 420

Are you looking down a microscope?
4:19 (4:15) – The tentacles, arranged in one or more rings around the mouth, bear stinging cells (**nematocysts**); either generally distributed over their surface or clumped together on the end. Tentacles do not have fine hairs (cilia). The body cavity of each individual polyp has but a single opening to the exterior that serves as both mouth and anus (Fig. 421)...Phylum **Cnidaria** **4:20**

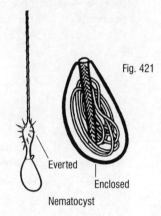

Fig. 421

Everted

Enclosed

Nematocyst

– The tentacles do not have nematocysts, but have fine hairs (cilia) throughout their length. Each individual zooid has a U-shaped gut, with a separate mouth and anus (although the latter may be very hard to see) **4:27**

4:20 (4:19) – The colony is composed of branching tubes which may bear smooth-sided cups (**hydrothecae**) at the tip and/or at intervals along their length. If cups are present, they are occupied by the individual polyps. If there are no cups, the polyps expand directly from the tubes of the colony. (Figs 424, 425). Hydroid ....
............................Sub-Phylum **Medusozoa**
Super-Class **Hydrozoa**
Class **Leptolida** **4:21**

– *Either*, the colony is not tubular *o r*, if it is, the sides of the cups are heavily ridged. (Figs 432, 434)
................................Sub-Phylum **Anthozoa**
Class **Hexacorallia** **4:25**

4:21 (4:20) – Each of the feeding polyps (**hydranths**) which make up most of the colony can retract more-or-less completely within its own hardened protective (chitinous) cup or **hydrotheca**. (Fig. 422)........Subclass **Leptothecatae** **4:22**

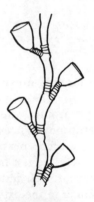

Fig. 422

– There are no protective cups on the colony which are large enough to enclose the retracted polyps. (Figs 423, 429) **4:24**

Fig. 423

4:22 (4:21) – The protective cups (hydrothecae) are bilaterally symmetrical *or*, if they are radially symmetrical, they are stalkless, being attached directly to the main stem of the colony (Fig. 424)...
....Order **Conica**
Sub-Orders **Campanulinida** and **Plumulariida**
(p. 85)

Fig. 424

– The protectice cups (hydrothecae) are radially symmetrical (but might have a dip on one side of the rim) and they are always stalked (Fig. 425)
....**4:23**

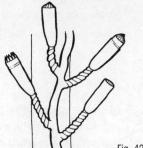

Fig. 425

4:23 (4.22) – The hydrothecal stalk is marked with a series of complete rings (Fig. 426) ....
Order **Proboscoidea**
Suborder **Campanulariida** (p. 85)

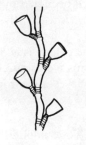

Fig. 426

– The hydrothecal stalk is either smooth or is incompletely ringed. (Fig. 427) ......Order **Conica**
Suborder **Lafoeida** (p. 85)

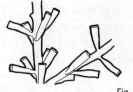

Fig. 427

4:24 (4:21) – A small hydrotheca, notably wider than long, is present (resembling a clergyman's dog-collar) but far too small to provide significant protection to the poly (hydranth) (Fig. 428) ....
............Subclass **Leptothecatae** Order **Conica** Suborder **Haleciida** (p. 85)

Fig. 428

– The colony is without hydrothecae. Only the polyp stalks are protected within the chitinous coenosarc so the polyps remain exposed at all times (Fig. 429) ....Subclass **Anthoathecatae** (p. 84)

Fig. 429

4:25 (4:20) – Numerous polyps arise at intervals from within an encrusting amorphous **coenchymatous** mass, typically itself encrusted with sand, etc. (Fig. 430). Perhaps the mass is enclosing a gastropod shell occupied by a hermit crab ....
.............................Order **Zoantharia** (p. 87)

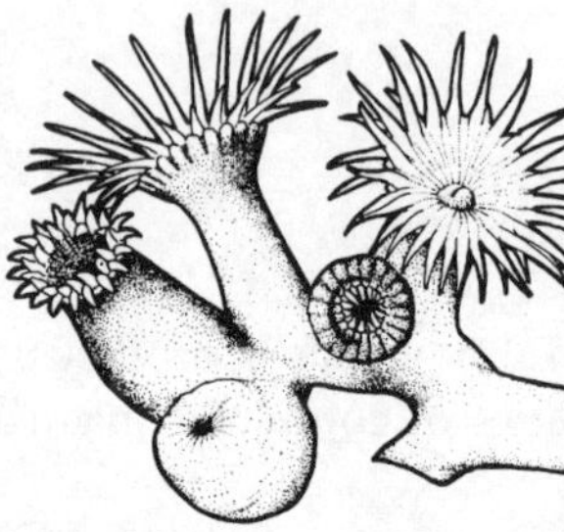

Fig. 430

– The colony is *either* a dense cluster of polyps, *or* it forms a structured coralline growth – but it never encloses a gastropod shell **4:26**

4:26 (4:25) – The colony does not have a calcareous skeleton but is a mass of sea anemones with knobbed tentacles (Fig. 431). Separation of the individual polyps may be incomplete so that individuals remain connected by a narrow strand of tissue. Colouration variable but often brilliant. jewel anemone *Corynactis viridis* ....
....................Order **Corallimorpharia** (p. 87)

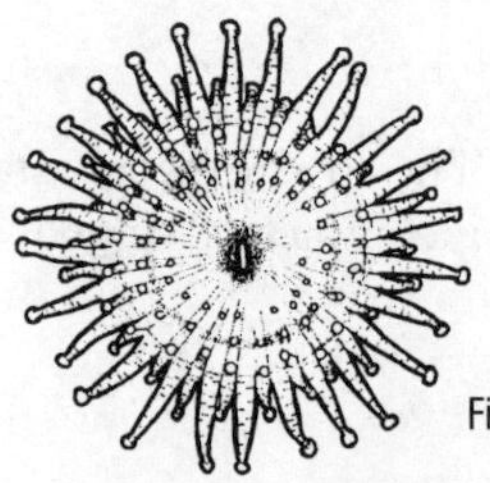

Fig. 431

– The colony is protected by an external calcareous skeleton (**corallum**) (Fig. 432). The polyp tentacles do not have knobbed ends. Stone coral ....
..............................Order **Scleractinia** (p. 88)

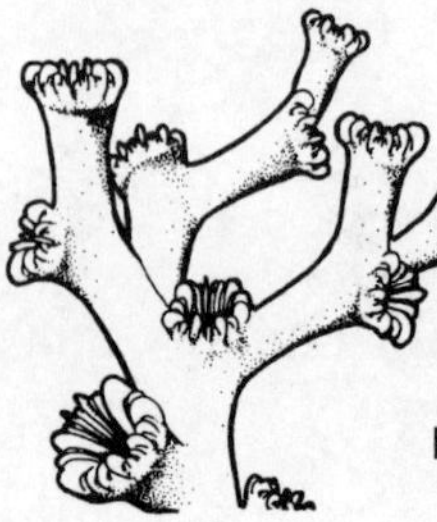

Fig. 432

Are you looking down a microscope?

4:27 (4:19) – Individual zooids, about 2mm in height, arise from a tube (stolon) that creeps over a hard substratum (Fig. 433), the whole colony appearing as a whitish fuzz on other encrusting organisms. The tentacles form an almost-closed horseshoe-shaped **lophophore** within which both mouth and anus open ....Phylum **Entoprocta** Order **Coloniales** (p. 120)

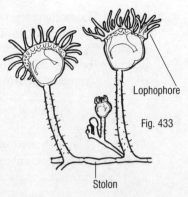

Lophophore

Fig. 433

Stolon

– Individual zooids may arise from a creeping tube-like stolon but, more typically, form a complex colony. Only the mouth opens within the circular ring of tentacles. The anus is outside, but very difficult to see! Sea mat .... Phylum **Bryozoa** **4:28**

4:28 (2:27) – The colony is calcified, at least in part; it may be erect, creeping or encrusting **4:29**

– The colony is not calcified but forms a fleshy or gelatinous encrustation (Fig. 434), a network of tubes (stolons) or dense erect tufts ....Class **Gymnolaemata** Order **Ctenostomatida** (p. 120)

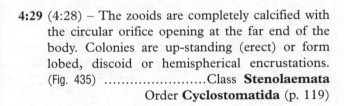

Fig. 434

4:29 (4:28) – The zooids are completely calcified with the circular orifice opening at the far end of the body. Colonies are up-standing (erect) or form lobed, discoid or hemispherical encrustations. (Fig. 435) ....Class **Stenolaemata** Order **Cyclostomatida** (p. 119)

– The zooids are often partly membranous with the orifice almost always closed by a 'trap-door' (**operculum**), and located down the side of the body. Colonies are erect, encrusting or creeping. (Fig. 436) ....Class **Gymnolaemata** Order **Cheilostomatida** (p. 120)

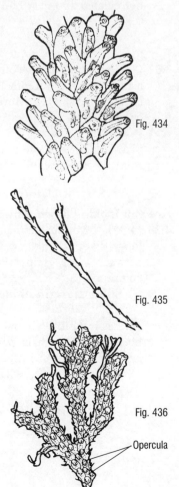

Fig. 435

Fig. 436

Opercula

4:30 (4:14) – The body resembles a small upside-down hand bell, attached to the substratum by the handle. Typically appears to have 8 'arms' linked together by a web. Moves by somersaulting. (Fig. 437). Stalked jellyfish ......Phylum **Cnidaria** Super-Class **Scyphozoa** Order **Stauromedusae** (p. 86)

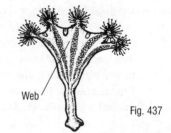

Web

Fig. 437

– The body is not shaped like an upside-down bell, and does not have 8 arms linked together by a web **4:31**

4:31 (4:30) – The specimen is an elongated, sausage or worm-shaped animal, with tentacles at one end, living in, or on the surface of, soft substrata...................**4:32**

– Specimen was attached to a hard substratum (which might be slightly buried in a soft one!). The common mouth/anus opens in the centre of the oral disc and is surrounded by at least one complete ring of retractable tentacles. The tentacles are not ciliated and bear batteries of stinging cells (nematocysts) ...Phylum **Cnidaria** Sub-Phylum **Anthozoa** Class **Hexacorallia** **4:35**

4:32 (4:31) – Skin leathery, often with tubercles and other bumps on the surface perhaps arranged in rows. Tentacles completely retractable, only extended when the animal is relaxed (Fig. 412). Mouth and anus terminal at opposite ends of the body. Sea cucumber ....Phylum **Echinodermata** Class **Holothuroidea** **4:12**

– Skin smooth and the body lacks an anus (or any other opening) at the end away from the tentacles ....Phylum **Cnidaria** **4:33**

Are you looking down a microscope?
4:33 (4:32) – Minute animal, only a few millimetres long, like a small *Hydra* living interstitially between sand grains (Fig. 438). May be locally common ....Sub-Phylum **Medusozoa** Subclass **Actinulidae** Order **Actinula** (p. 84)

Fig. 438

– An easily visible animal living in a mucus-lined burrow, rather than between sand grains. Sea anemone ....Sub-Phylum **Anthozoa** Class Hexacorallia **4:34**

4:34 (4:33) – Sea anemone with two series of tentacles; short ones arising from the mouth (oral tentacles) and much longer ones from the periphery of the disc (marginal tentacles) (Fig. 439). Adults live in tubes buried in a soft substratum [**Note:** that the fragile tube is often destroyed when the animal is extracted.] ....Order **Ceriantharia** (p. 87)

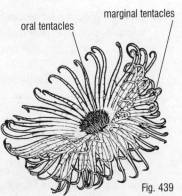

oral tentacles   marginal tentacles

Fig. 439

– Sea anemone with one series of tentacles, all arising from the periphery of the disc (Fig. 440), perhaps in several whorls. Adults burrow but do not secrete tubes. Burrowing anemone ....
..................................Order **Actiniaria** (p.87)

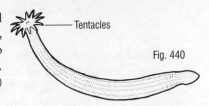

Tentacles

Fig. 440

4:35 (4:31) – The specimen is a polyp with a calcareous skeleton, permanently fixed in position on a hard substratum (Fig. 441). Solitary coral ....
..............................Order **Scleractinia** (p. 88)

– The specimen is a polyp which lacks any kind of calcareous skeleton. It may be capable of gliding very slowly over the substratum. Sea anemone
....**4:36**

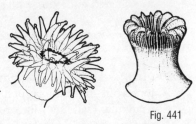

Fig. 441

4:36 (4:35) – An anemone with knobbed tentacles (Fig. 442). Colouration variable but often brilliant. The jewel anemone *Corynactis viridis* ....
.....................Order **Corallimorpharia** (p. 87)

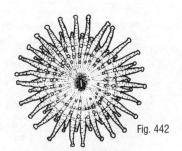

Fig. 442

– Tentacles of the anemone lack knobs on the end (Fig. 443). A true sea anemone ....
..............................Order **Actiniaria** (p. 87)

Fig. 443

4:37 (4:1) – Specimen passively floating on or near the surface, perhaps suspended from a float ....
.........................Phylum **Cnidaria** **4:38**

–   Specimen free-swimming or floating within the water column **4:40**

4:38 (4:37) – The specimen looks like a small sea anemone, with a tubular main body (the column) and short stubby tentacles (lengthening with age), floating almost immobile at the surface of the sea in summer (Fig. 444). Arachnactis larva ....
......Sub-Phylum **Anthozoa** Class **Hexacorallia**
Order **Ceriantharia** (p. 87)

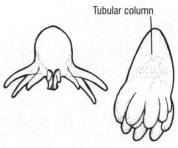

Fig. 444

–   Specimen appears to be a complex organism with many tentacles hanging down into the water from an obvious float. (Fig. 449, Fig. 450) ....
..............................Sub-Phylum **Medusozoa**
Super-Class **Hydrozoa** **4:39**

NOTE: If the specimen does not look like any of these alternatives proceed to couplet 4:41

4:39 (4:38) – The deep blue, raft-like float (up to 10cm long but may be much smaller) has a stiff triangular sail set diagonally across the upper surface. Short tentacles hang down into the water from the float. Often cast ashore on SW-facing beaches in SW Britain: the colourless skeleton of the float and sail persists after the animal has decomposed. An open sea (pelagic) hydroid colony: the by-the-wind sailor, *Velella velella* (Fig. 445) ....Class **Leptolida**
Subclass **Anthoathecatae** (p. 84)

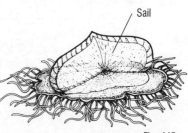

Fig. 445

–   The floppy float, often much more than 10cm long, may resemble a partly-inflated polythene bag, but does not bear a distinct sail. Very long tentacles, armed with powerful stinging cells, hang down from the float (Fig. 446). Portuguese man o' war, *Physalia physalis* ....
..........................Class **Siphonophora** (p. 86)

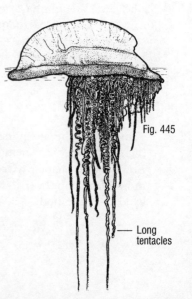

Fig. 445

Long tentacles

4:40 (4:37) – The specimen appears to be a polymorphic colony (ie. consisting of 'individuals' of different types) suspended from one or (many) more floats and trailing long tentacles through the water. (Fig. 447) Siphonophore ....
...Phylum **Cnidaria** Class **Siphonophora** (p. 86)

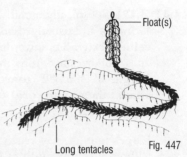

Float(s)

Long tentacles   Fig. 447

– The specimen appears to be an individual animal **4:41**

4:41 (4:40) – Body shape remains constant as the animal swims, which it does by beating fine hairs (**cilia**) rather than by contraction of muscles in the body wall. Either without tentacles or may have two long tentacles trailing in the water behind it **4:42**

– Specimen swims by extending and contracting its umbrella-like body. Typically with more than 2 tentacles. Jellyfish ....Phylum **Cnidaria** Sub-Phylum **Medusozoa** **4:44**

4:42 (4:41) – The globular transparent body bears two tentacles (look carefully: the tentacles are completely retractile but, when withdrawn, they are usually visible as white threads within the 'body') ....Class **Tentaculata** **4:43**

– The adult's body resembles that of an airship (Fig. 448). The animal is without tentacles at all stages of its life cycle ....Class **Nuda** Order **Beroida** (p. 88)

Fig. 448

4:43 (4:42) – Body approximately spherical (perhaps an elongated sphere?) (Fig. 449). The tentacles are both much longer than the body. Sea gooseberry ....Order **Cydippida** (p. 88)

NOTE: With an obvious gut running straight through the middle

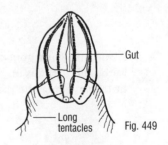

Gut

Long tentacles   Fig. 449

– Body rocket-shaped with large lobes around the mouth (oral lobes). (Fig. 450). The tentacles are not as long as the body ....Order **Lobata** (p. 88)

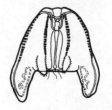

Fig. 450

4:44 (4:42) – Typically small, less than 20mm in diameter (but *Aequorea* may reach 175mm), and usually almost transparent. A jellyfish with a shelf of tissue (called the **velum**) extending inwards from the margin of the bell. The mouth typically hangs on a hollow stalk from the inside surface of the bell. The tentacles around the margin of the bell (**marginal tentacles**) are always longer than any tentacles around the mouth (**oral tentacles**). The medusa of a hydroid = a hydromedusa ....Super-Class **Hydrozoa** **4:45**

–   Large, (adults may reach 1m diameter) and often brightly coloured. A jellyfish without a velum. With or without marginal tentacles. Oral tentacles may be much longer than marginal tentacles. True jellyfish = a scyphomedusa ....Super-Class **Scyphozoa** **4:49**

4:45 (4:44) – A medusa with four (or occasionally more) conspicuous cylindrical tubes (**radial canals**), within the structure of the bell, radiating outwards from the centre towards the margin. Peripheral tentacles arise from the margin of the bell (**marginal tentacles**). (Fig. 452, Fig. 453) **4:46**

–   A medusa without radial canals (Fig. 451). Peripheral tentacles arise from the upper surface of the bell, not from the margin ....Subclass **Narcomedusae** Order **Narcomedusa** (p. 83)

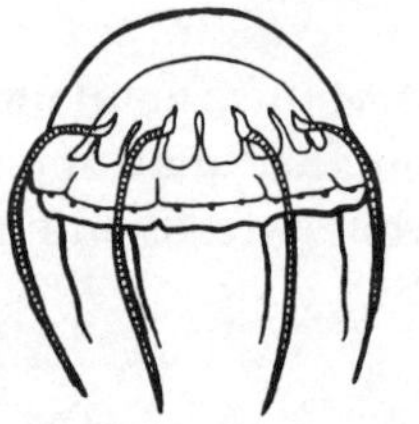

Fig. 451

4:46 (4:45) – A medusa with dark thickenings (the gonads) only on the walls of the radial canals (Fig. 452) **4:47**

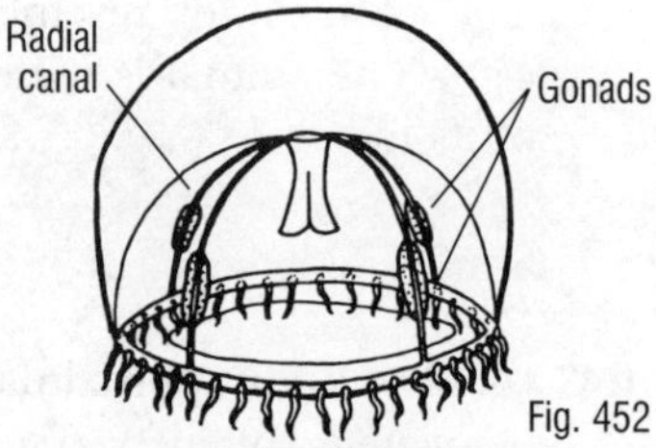

Radial canal

Gonads

Fig. 452

–   A medusa with gonads on the stomach (Fig. 453) (although perhaps on the stomach and extending a little way along the radial canals) **4:48**

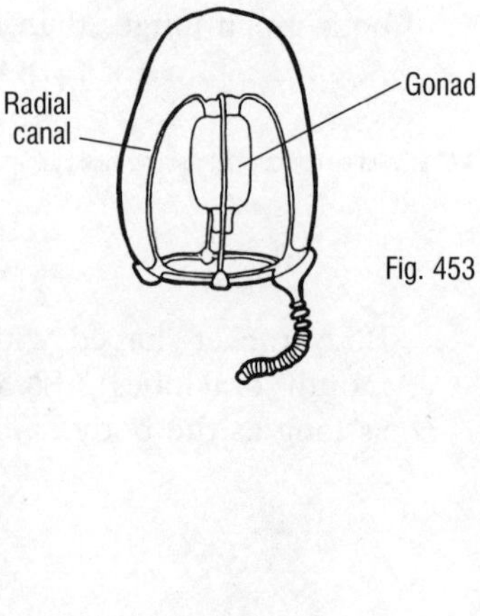

Radial canal

Gonad

Fig. 453

4:47 (4:46) – A medusa in the form of a tall bell (Fig. 454) bearing sensory 'clubs' (**statocysts**) Trachymedusa ....Subclass **Trachymedusae** Order **Trachymedusa** (p. 84)

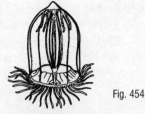

Fig. 454

– A medusa in the form of a somewhat flattened umbrella (Fig. 255). Any **statocysts**, if present, are in the velum and do not form sensory clubs. Leptomedusa ...Subclass **Leptothecatae** (p. 85)

Fig. 455

4:48 (4:46) – A medusa from brackish water, typically in the shape of an inverted-bowl with many marginal tentacles. (Fig. 456). **Statocysts**, if present, are in the form of sensory clubs. Limnomedusa ....Subclass **Limnomedusae** Order **Limnomedusa** (p. 83)

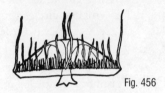

Fig. 456

– A medusa from saline water, tall and bell-shaped in form, without **statocysts** and with only a few marginal tentacles. (Although usually more than the one shown in Fig. 457). Anthomedusa ....Subclass **Anthoathecatae** (p. 84)

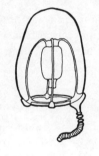

Fig. 457

4:49 (4:44) – A jellyfish with marginal tentacles and with a single, central, mouth **4:50**

– A jellyfish without marginal tentacles and, in place of a single mouth, there are 8 oral arms hanging below the umbrella, on which there are numerous mouth openings. (Fig. 258). *Rhizostoma octopus* ... .Order **Rhizostomae** (p. 86)

Fig. 458

4:50 (4:49) – A small, probably brightly-coloured, jellyfish in which the outer surface of the bell is divided into upper and lower regions by what appears to be a tightly pulled draw-string (the coronal groove) (Fig. 459). Mouth simple ....
............................Order **Coronatae** (p. 86)

Fig. 459

– A jellyfish without a 'drawstring' and with the corners of the mouth drawn out into four frilly lobes. (Fig. 460). May be large (100cm!), may be brightly coloured, or may be transparent except for 4 mauve circles (gonads) ....
.......................Order **Semaeostomae** (p. 86)

Fig. 460

KEY 5

A KEY TO BILATERALLY-SYMMETRICAL ANIMALS WITH JOINTED LEGS

Arthropods

All the keys were written for field biologists with, on occasion, limited laboratory support in the way of binocular microscopes, and the assumption is made that the specimen is alive, and is being viewed under sea water, unless some comment is made to the contrary. **Bold type** in the text indicates terms that are defined in the glossary (p. 144).

5:1 – Animal attached to rocks, shells, seaweeds, floating objects or the skin of some larger animal. Perhaps an **ectoparasite**, burrowing into the skin or shell of its host: even an **endoparasite** in a 'crab', visible externally as a finely-granular mass (the externa) under the abdomen **5:2**

– Animal not attached, could move around **5:14**

5:2 (5:1) – Animal free living (i.e., living as a separate entity and not in any way parasitic), typically cemented to an inanimate substratum but perhaps on a shell, associated with a sponge or with a solitary coral, or burrowing within an empty snail shell now occupied by a hermit crab. Barnacle ....
Phylum **Arthropoda** Sub-Phylum **Crustacea** Class **Cirripedia** **5:3**

– Animal living on (or partially inside) the body of another living animal **5:5**

5:3 (5.2) – The animal's body is hidden within (protected by) a series of calcareous plates ....
...............................Order **Thoracica** **5:4**

– The animal's body is hidden within (protected by) the inside surface of an empty whelk shell occupied by a hermit crab. Presence of the burrowing barnacle is revealed by small dark slits visible in the shell's central column (**columella**) (Fig. 501) ....Order **Acrothoracica** (p. 124)

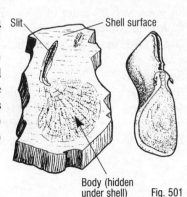

Slit Shell surface

Body (hidden under shell)   Fig. 501

Table 5.1. The jointed legs of the shore crab *Carcinus maenas* as an example of the way in which the appendages of the different somites have become adapted to serve different functions in crustaceans. The functions vary from group to group. A shrimp or prawn, for example, would use its pleopods for swimming.

Somite	Appendage	Tagma	Function	
1	nil			
2	1st Antennae		Sensory	
3	2nd Antennae	Head	Sensory	
4	Mandibles		Cut up the food and pass it into the mouth	
5	1st Maxillae		Hold food for mandibles to cut	
6	2nd Maxillae		Pass food to mandibles	
7	1st Maxillipeds		Pass food to the maxillae	
8	2nd Maxillipeds		Pass food to the maxillae	
9	3rd Maxillipeds		Grasp food, manipulate it and pass it forward (looks like inward) to the other mouthparts	
10	Chelae or 1st Pereiopods	Thorax	Offence/Defence. Pick up / tear off pieces of food and pass them to the maxillipeds	
11	2nd Pereiopods		Walking	
12	3rd Pereiopods		Walking	
13	4th Pereiopods		Walking	
14	5th Pereiopods		Walking	
			—— Male ——	—— Female ——
15	1st Pleopods		Copulatory styles	absent
16	2nd Pleopods		Copulatory styles	carry eggs
17	3rd Pleopods	Abdomen	absent	carry eggs
18	4th Pleopods		absent	carry eggs
19	5th Pleopods		absent	carry eggs
20	nil			

It is more complicated than this. Primitively, each appendage had an exopodite and an endopodite (outer and inner branches respectively). The exopodites of thoracic legs often function as gills whilst endopodites form legs or nippers. Primitive crustacea may have enjoyed 32 pairs of gills – four to each thoracic somite. Advanced forms, such as *C. maenas*, have only 9 pairs: a podobranch on maxillipeds 2 and 3; arthrobranchs on 2nd & 3rd maxillipeds and chelae; pleurobranchs on pereiopods 2 and 3.

Synonyms

Antennules	=	1st Antennae	Antennae	=	2nd Antennae
Maxillules	=	1st Maxillae	Maxillae	=	2nd Maxillae
Chelipeds	=	Chelae	Pleiopods	=	Pleopods
Peraeopods	=	Pereiopods	Swimmerettes	=	Pleopods

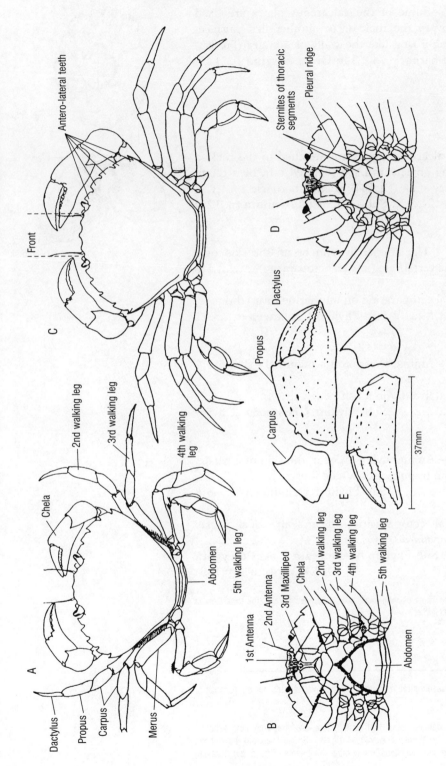

Fig. 502 The external features of *Carcinus maenas*.
(a) Female, dorsal surface. (b) Female, ventral surface. (c) Male, dorsal surface. (d) Male, ventral surface. (e) Chelae of a large male; it is impossible to see the true shape of the chelae in (a) or (b) because of the angle at which they are held. Drawings by Marilyn Crothers from Crothers (1967).

5:4 (5:3) – Some of the calcareous plates are fixed
directly to the rock or to another firm surface,
forming a ring like the walls of a crater (Fig. 503)
Acorn barnacle ......Sub-Order **Sessilia** (p. 123)

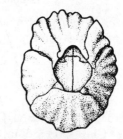

Fig. 503

– The calcareous plates are attached to the rock, a
floating object, or a self-secreted raft, by a tough
leathery stalk (Fig. 504) Stalked barnacle ....
.....................Sub-Order **Pedunculata** (p. 123)

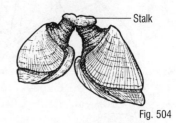

Stalk

Fig. 504

5:5 (5:2) – The animal lives in or on the skin of a
marine vertebrate (it is an ectoparasite)[5] **5:6**

– Animal ectoparasitic on an marine invertebrate ...
.....................Sub-Phylum **Crustacea** **5:11**

5:6 (5:5) – Animal lives in/on a mammal's skin ...**5:7**

– Animal lives in/on a fish ....
.....................Sub-Phylum **Crustacea** **5:9**

5:7 (5:6) – Animal living on or in the skin of a whale,
dolphin or porpoise. Whale louse ....
.....................Sub-Phylum **Crustacea** **5:8**

– Animal ectoparasitic on a seal[6]. Seal louse.
Echinophthirius horridus ....
.........Sub-Phylum **Atelocerata** Class **Pterygota**
Order **Anoplura** (p.135)

NOTE: A wingless insect (sucking louse) with three pairs of legs. The three thoracic
somites are fused together

[5] [Parasites of seabirds are regarded as 'land invertebrates' for the purpose of
this key]

[6] Dead seals, stranded above high water mark, are effectively land habitats.
Larvae of the fly *Kimosina empirica* (Diptera Sphaeroceridae) have been
recorded therein and, doubtless, many other inhabitants of dead and decaying
flesh *could* occur.

5:8 (5:7) – Animal recognisable as a crustacean, with jointed legs and a body clearly composed of distinct somites **5:10**

– Animal recognisable as a crustacean only whilst feeding, when the jointed legs are displayed. Perhaps looks like Fig. 505. Barnacle ....
......Class **Cirripedia** Order **Thoracica**[7] (p.123)

Fig. 505

5:9 (5:6) – Animal with 7 pairs of thoracic appendages (plus the maxillipeds which appear to be head appendages), the first two and last three of which are claw-like (**subchelate**). Eyes and antennules vestigial. Abdomen vestigial (Fig. 506) ....
......................................Class **Malacostraca**
Order **Amphipoda** Family **Cyamidae** (p.130)

Claw

Fig. 506

– Animal with 5 pairs of thoracic legs (plus the maxillipeds ditto), none of which is claw-like (subchelate). Eyes and antennules functional. The narrow abdomen ends in **caudal furca** (Fig. 507) ...Class **Copepoda** Order **Harpacticoida** (p.126)

NOTE: Up to 60 cm in length, but mostly less than 3 mm, living mainly on the baleen plates of whalebone whales

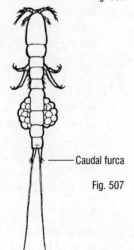

Caudal furca

Fig. 507

---

[7] *Xenobalanus* lives on porpoises and fin whales, *Coronula* on humpback whales and *Conchoderma* (illustrated) on various species of whale and (rarely) on other floating objects.

5:10 (5:8) – Head with a pair of large eyes. Thoracic somites 3-5 fused together. The abdomen has 5 somites + a telson, which does not end in a caudal furca. (Fig. 508). Praniza larva of a gnathid ....Class **Isopoda** (p. 129)

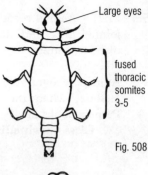

Fig. 508

– The enlarged head is without paired eyes. There are 8 free somites + a telson behind the head. The narrow abdomen typically ends in a caudal furca. (Fig. 509) ....Class **Copepoda**[8](p. 125)

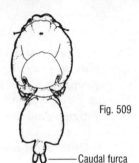

Fig. 509

5:11 (5:5)– Animal recognisable as a crustacean, with jointed legs and somited body; not associated with jellyfish or sponges **5:12**

– Animal a globular mass or only recognisable as a crustacean whilst feeding, when the jointed legs are displayed. Barnacle ...Class **Cirripedia 5:13**

5:12 (5:11) – Animal attached to the *abdomen* of a hermit crab (*Pagurus bernhardus* or *Anapagurus laevis*). Seven pairs of thoracic legs. Females up to 11mm long, perhaps with parasitic (4mm long) males on the thorax. Telson without a caudal furca (Fig. 510). *Athelges paguri* ....
......Class **Malacostraca** Order **Isopoda** (p. 129)

Fig. 510

– Animal a parasite or commensal of an opisthobranch or bivalve mollusc, of an echinoderm, an annelid worm, an ascidian, a mysid, a crab or a lobster – but not attached to the abdomen. The, typically enlarged, head is without paired eyes. There are 8 free somites behind the head, and a telson. The narrow abdomen typically ends in a caudal furca. Never with parasitic males on the thorax (Fig. 511) ......Class **Copepoda** (p. 125)[8]

Fig. 511

[8] Many parasitic and commensal copepods have grossly-reduced morphology and are often unrecognisable as crustaceans. Only the production of a pair of external ovisacs, on maturity, betrays their copepodan nature.

5.13 (5.11) – Animal may not be truly parasitic but lives embedded in the skin / integument of its host. When actively feeding, jointed legs are visible and the animal is clearly a barnacle. (Fig. 512) ....
....Order **Thoracica**
Sub-Order **Sessilia** (p. 123)[9]

–   Animal appears as a smooth or slightly-granular mass (externa), lacking legs or any other crustacean feature, attached to the abdomen of a decapod crustacean, often a crab. (Fig. 513) ....
.........**Cirripedia** Order **Rhizocephala** (p. 124)

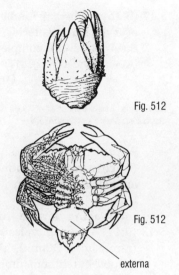

Fig. 512

Fig. 512

externa

5:14 (5:1) – Head with a pair of antennae, and/or of antennules **5:15**

–   Head with neither antennules nor antennae ......
.....................................Phylum **Arthropoda**
Sub-Phylum **Chelicerata** **5:37**

5:15 (5.14) – Animal with a carapace (a fold of skin which grows out and over at least part of the thorax) hiding the underlying somites from view
.....................................Phylum **Arthropoda**
Sub-Phylum **Crustacea** (in part) **5:16**

–   Animal without a carapace: all thoracic and abdominal somites are clearly visible from above, although the first thoracic somite may be fused with the head **5:28**

5:16 (5:15) – The carapace more or less encloses the body in a globular or bivalved shell. (Fig. 514, Fig. 515, Fig. 516, Fig. 517, Fig. 518) **5:17**

–   The carapace is never bivalved and it covers only the head and thorax, leaving most, or all, of the abdomen free. **NOTE**, however, that some of these crustacea (crabs, porcelain crabs and squat lobsters) habitually wrap their abdomen around and tuck it up underneath the thorax. (Fig. 502) ...
........................Class **Malacostraca** **5:21**

---

[9] *Alepas parasitica*, citron yellow in colour, lives on jelly fish: *Acasta spongites* and *Balanus spongicola* live embedded in sponge.

5:17 (5:16) – The large inflated carapace extends back over the front (anterior) part of the abdomen (but does not cover it completely) and has a hinged flap over the head. (Fig. 514) ......Class **Malacostraca** Order **Leptostraca** (p. 127)

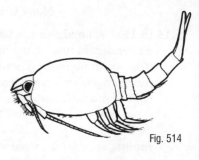

Fig. 514

NOTE: None of the 8 pairs of thoracic legs end in claws (ie. are not **chelate**) nor are modified into feeding arms (**maxillipeds**)

– Animal totally enclosed in a hinged bivalve shell (when at rest). When moving, it may resemble an animated broad bean **5:18**

Are you looking down a microscope ?

5:18 (5:17) – Animal typically less than 8mm in length (rarely up to 30mm). Typically, the shell is bean-shaped but is sometimes pointed at one or both ends. The single median eye, if present, is close to the upper (dorsal) edge of the carapace. [Paired eyes are only present in the large (20+ mm) *Macrocypris*]. When the valves are open, the paired antennules and antennae can protrude from the front (out of the mantle cavity) and three pairs of thoracic legs from the back end. Without an accumulation of lipid droplets. (Fig. 516, Fig. 517, Fig. 518) ....Class **Ostracoda** **5:19**

– Animal 1-2 mm in length, often dark brown in colour. Shell rounded to a blunt point at the head end, and tapering at the other end. A median eye may be visible, whilst the paired compound eyes are prominent. When the valves are open, a single pair of antennules (but not antennae) can be protruded from the front, with six pairs of thoracic legs, plus a pair of uniramous caudal appendages, from the back end. The body always contains an accumulation of lipid droplets. Initially free-swimming but, later, becoming attached to the substratum (Fig. 515). Cypris larva of a barnacle ... .Class **Cirripedia** (p. 123)

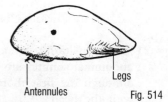

Antennules   Legs

Fig. 514

5:19 (5:18) – The valves are of equal size (equivalve). The carapace may reach 30mm, with or without a deep indentation in the front region below the rostrum (rostral incisure), through which the animal extends its antennae for swimming ...**5:20**

– The valves are different sizes (inequivalve) so that the right overlaps the left around the entire margin. The carapace, typically less than 1mm long, is ovate in outline and always lacks a 'rostral incisure'. (Fig. 516) ...Order **Platycopida** (p. 125)

Fig. 516

5:20 (5:19) – Carapace up to 30mm long, with or without a deep indentation at the front but always with a convex lower (ventral) margin. The outer surface is weakly calcified, smooth, thin and flexible. (Fig. 517) ...Order **Myodocopida** (p. 125)

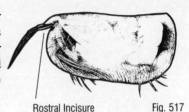

Rostral Incisure   Fig. 517

– Carapace up to 8mm long, but typically less than 1mm, without an anterior rostral incisure. Ventral margin straight or concave: never convex. The outer surface is strongly calcified and rigid; ornamented or smooth. (Fig. 518) ....
...........................Order **Podocopida** (p. 125)

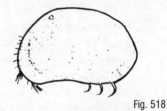

Fig. 518

5:21 (5:16) – Carapace covers the whole of the thorax: no thoracic somites are visible in dorsal view. (Figs 519-523) **5:22**

NOTE: The thoracic somites bear the pereiopods (chelae and walking legs) whilst abdominal somites bear pleopods (swimming legs) Fig. 502B

– Carapace does not cover the whole of the thorax ; one, at least, of the thoracic somites is visible to top (dorsal) view. (Figs 524-528) **5:24**

5:22 (5:21) – When extended, the abdomen stretches straight-out behind the thorax and is bilaterally symmetrical **5:23**

–   Abdomen of the animal is *either* coiled up to one side behind the thorax and often hidden inside a snail shell e.g. hermit crab (Fig. 519) or it is tucked up underneath the thorax (crab or squat lobster) (Fig. 520) ....Order **Decapoda**[10] (p. 131)

Fig. 519

Fig. 520

5:23 (5:22) – All of the eight pairs of thoracic legs (those of appendages beneath the carapace) are similar: none has claws (ie. it is not **chelate**) nor is it modified as a feeding arm (**maxilliped**). (Fig. 521). Typically with iridescent photophores on the ventral surface of the abdomen. Krill ....
........................Order **Euphausiacea** (p. 130)

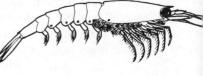

Fig. 521

–   It is obvious that the animal does not have 8 similar pairs of thoracic legs. The first three pairs are modified as feeding arms (maxillipeds) (and often difficult to see) whilst the fourth is modified as the 'nippers' (chelae), so leaving only 5 for moving around. Other legs may also have claws (ie. are chelate). (Fig. 522, Fig. 523). Lobsters, crawfish, shrimps and prawns ....
...............................Order **Decapoda** (p. 131)

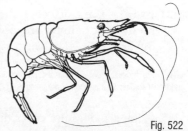

Fig. 522

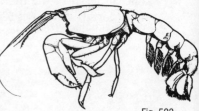

Fig. 523

---

[10] If your specimen is a large crab or lobster, it might be worth looking at the mouthparts under a microscope. Funch & Kristensen (1995) have proposed a new Phylum, Class, Order and Family for *Symbion pandora* which they described from the mouthparts of *Nephrops norvegica*. See Phylum Cycliophora p. 121.

5:24 (5:21) – Head and the first 2 thoracic somites are distinct in front of the fused thoracic somites 3-5 (Fig. 524), which can be easily mistaken for a carapace. Praniza larva or an adult female gnathid isopod ....Order **Isopoda** (p.129)

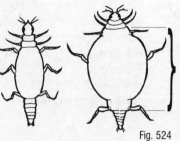

Fused
thoracic
somites
3-5

Fig. 524

– Carapace covers at least the first 2 thoracic somites **5:25**

5:25 (5:24) – Most of the thorax is visible to top (dorsal) view: the carapace covers fewer than the first four somites. (Fig. 525, Fig. 526) **5:26**

– Most of the thorax is hidden from top (dorsal) view: the carapace covers at least the first four somites. (Fig. 532, Fig. 533) **5:27**

Are you looking down a microscope ?

5:26 (5:25) – There are six pairs of walking legs, and six visible thoracic somites, behind the carapace, which covers only the first two somites. The 1st pair of thoracic legs are feeding arms (maxillipeds) and difficult to see but the 2nd have conspicuous claws (chelae). (Fig. 525) ....
..........................Order **Tanaidacea** (p. 129)

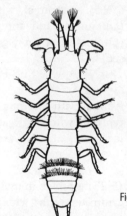

Fig. 525

– There are five pairs of walking legs and five visible thoracic somites behind the carapace, which covers the first 3 thoracic somites. There are no claws (chelae) (Fig. 526) ....
..............................Order **Cumacea** (p. 129)

Fig. 526

NOTE: The general appearance is often tadpole-like

5:27 (5:25) – Carapace covers the first 4 thoracic somites – leaving the other 4 free. Only the last 3 pairs of thoracic legs function as walking legs as the first 5 pairs are clawed feeding arms (chelate maxillipeds), the 2nd of which is enormously developed (Fig. 527). The uropods do not have conspicuous **statocysts**. Mantis shrimp ....Order **Stomatopoda** (p. 128)

Fig. 527

–   Carapace covers almost all of the thoracic somites – but at least the last is visible in dorsal view. None of the 8 pairs of thoracic legs is chelate and all are similar (Fig. 528). The **statocysts** are conspicuous as circles in the uropods. (Fig. 529). Opossum shrimp ....Order **Mysidacea** (p. 128)

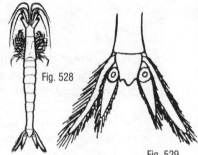

Fig. 528

Fig. 529

NOTE: Females have a very conspicuous brood pouch

5:28 (5:15) – Animal with two pairs of antennae (antennules and antennae) and with two-armed (biramous) appendages (which may be hard to see) ....Phylum **Arthropoda**
Sub-Phylum **Crustacea** **5:29**

–   Animal with one pair of antennae (or none) and typically with single-armed (**uniramous**) walking legs **5:31**

5:29 (5:28) – Small animal (only a few species are over 2mm in length) with an elongated head (actually head + first thoracic somite) followed by 9 thoracic somites and a telson. Body cylindrical or flattened top-to-bottom (dorso-ventrally). Often with greatly elongated antennules, with which it swims. (Fig. 530). Five pairs of 'swimming legs' on the free thoracic somites. No legs on the abdominal somites ......Class **Copepoda** (p. 125)

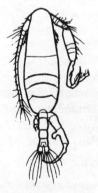

Fig. 530

NOTE: The only species likely to exceed 2mm in length are in the Order **Calanoida**

–   Head not greatly elongated, and followed by more than 9 visible somites. (Fig. 531, Fig. 532) Never swims by the use of its head appendages. Abdominal legs typically present and used for that purpose ....Class **Malacostraca** **5:30**

5:30 (5:29) – Animal flattened from top to bottom. Walking legs typically all similar and pointed downwards and backwards. (Fig. 531) only the first pair, if any, bear nippers ....
...................................Order **Isopoda** (p. 129)

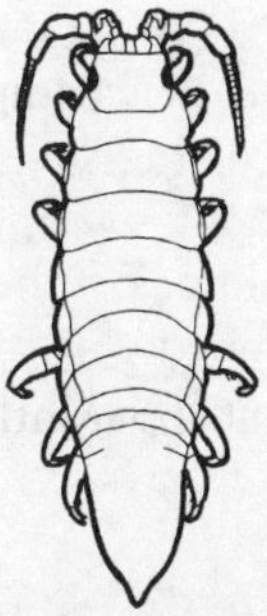

Fig. 531

– Animal flattened from side to side. Legs dissimilar. Typically, the first two pairs bear nippers. They, and the next two pairs, point backwards. The last three pairs point forwards. (Fig. 532) ....
...........................Order **Amphipoda** (p. 130)

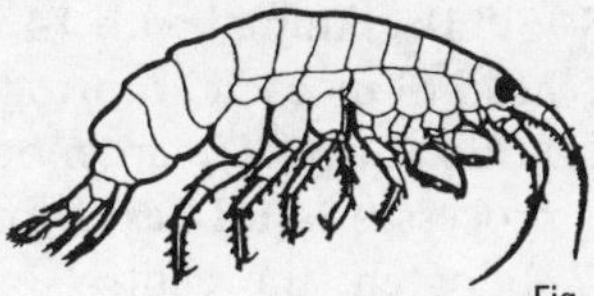

Fig. 532

5:31 (5:28) – Animal, long-bodied with many more than 4 pairs of walking legs ......Phylum **Arthropoda** Sub-Phylum **Atelocerata** **5:32**

– Animal with only 3 or 4 pairs of walking legs ......
....**5:33**

5:32 (5:31) – Animal with a cylindrical body. Up to 20mm long but only 0.5mm diameter. The numerous somites each appear to bear two pairs of walking legs. (Fig. 533). No poison fangs. Millipede *Thalassiobates littoralis* ....Class **Diplopoda** Order **Julida** (p. 133)

Fig. 533

– Animal with a top-to-bottom (dorso-ventrally) flattened body. The trunk somites each bear a single pair of walking legs, except the first (which has a pair of poison fangs) and the last two. (Fig. 534) Centipede ....Class **Chilopoda** Order **Geophilida** (p. 134)

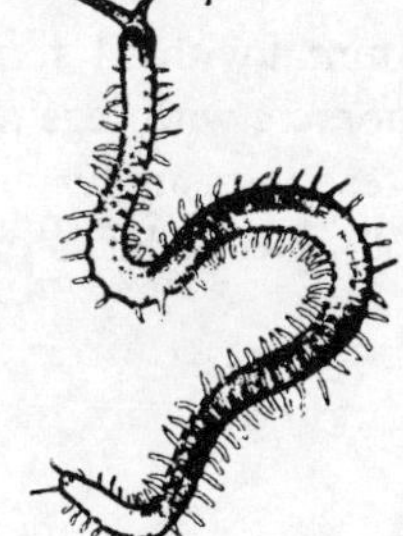

Fig. 534

5:33 (5:31) – Animal with 3 pairs of walking legs and, perhaps, one or two pairs of wings. Insect ....
...................................Phylum **Arthropoda** Sub-Phylum **Atelocerata** **5:34**

– Animal with four pairs of walking legs, and no wings **5:37**

5:34 (5:33) – Animal with wings (Fig. 535) and may be able to fly. Adult insect[11] ....
.............................Class **Pterygota** (p. 135)

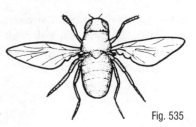

Fig. 535

– Animal apparently without wings and unable to fly
....**5:35**

5.35 (5:34) – Animal with 14 visible somites behind the head (3 thoracic, bearing legs, and 11 abdominal). Long, hair-like, antennae. Three long, hair-like processes (**anal cerci**) project from the end of the abdomen: the central one longer than the outer two. (Fig. 536). Bristletail ....Class **Apterygota**
Order **Archaeognatha** (p. 134)

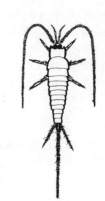

Fig. 536

– Animal with 11 or fewer somites visible behind the head. Without long hair-like antennae or anal cerci
....**5:36**

5:36 (5:35)– Animal with 9 somites visible behind the head (3 thoracic, bearing legs, plus six abdominal). Short, stumpy, antennae with 4 segments. (Fig. 537). Springtail ....
.............................Class **Collembola** (p. 134)

Fig. 537

– Animal with 11 somites visible behind the head (3 thoracic with legs plus 8 abdominal). Antennae, if present, usually with more than 4 segments (Fig. 538). Beetle larva or pupa ....Class **Pterygota**
Order **Coleoptera** (p. 135)

Fig. 538

---

[11] Almost any flying insect might appear on the shore. Some of the test panel suggested that the key should proceed to ordinal level, as is done for all other Classes. But to do so would simply duplicate keys E and F in Tilling (1987). Only beetles (Order Coleoptera) and true flies (Order Diptera) have any significant number of marine representatives.

5:37 (5:33) – Small animal, up to 3.5mm long, with a large, prominent, pair of chelae; bigger than the other three pairs of walking legs. Abdomen much larger than the thorax, somites discrete. (Fig. 539). False scorpion *Neobisium maritimum* ....
............Phylum **Arthropoda** Class **Arachnida** Order **Pseudoscorpiones** (p. 132)

Fig. 539

– Chelae, if present, much smaller than the walking legs. If abdomen is larger than the thorax, no somites are visible **5:38**

5:38 – Body divided into cephalothorax and abdomen, joined by a narrow waist (pedicel). Somites of the cephalothorax covered by a carapace and hidden from dorsal view. Abdomen unsomited. (Fig. 540). Spider ...Phylum **Arthropoda** Class **Arachnida** Order **Aranea** (p. 131)

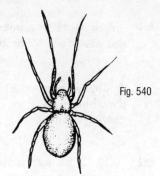

Fig. 540

– Body not divided into two halves with a narrow waist between them **5:39**

5:39 – Walking legs typically shorter than the length of the body, which is not obviously somited, although the surface may be divided up into different regions. (Fig. 541). Mite ......Phylum **Arthropoda** Class **Arachnida** Order **Acariformes** (p. 132)

NOTE: A very small animal; few species reach 2mm in length

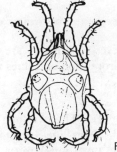

Fig. 541

– Walking legs typically much longer than the body[12], which is obviously somited. (Fig. 542). Sea spider ....Phylum **Pycnogonida** (p. 136)

Fig. 542

---

[12] The species illustrated, *Pycnogonum littorale*, has much shorter legs than the other British species.

KEY 6

A KEY TO ANIMALS WITH A SHELL

All the keys were written for field biologists with, on occasion, limited laboratory support in the way of binocular microscopes, and the assumption is made that the specimen is alive, and is being viewed under sea water, unless some comment is made to the contrary. **Bold type** in the text indicates terms that are defined in the glossary (p. 144).

6:1 – Animal with an internal shell that may be felt by applying gentle pressure to the dorsal surface of the body, which is typically dome-shaped ....
....Phylum **Mollusca** 6:2

–   Animal with an external shell, although not necessarily one large enough to contain the whole body. Part, or all, of the shell may be covered by the **mantle** of an actively moving animal 6:8

6:2 (6:1) – The animal has conspicuous large eyes. It 'swims' by jet propulsion. The animal has 2 tentacles (on which the suckers are clustered into a 'club' at the distal end) in addition to the 8 arms, which bear suckers along their whole length ......
....Class **Cephalopoda** 6:3

NOTE: The streamlined body bears fins along each side. Capable of rapid colour / pattern changes

–   Eyes, if present, are not large or conspicuous; the animal does not swim by jet propulsion and does not have 8 arms, bearing suckers, growing out from the head
....Class **Gastropoda** 6:4

6:3 (6:2) – The two long tentacles (much longer than the arms) are retractable into pits. The lateral fins do not (quite) meet at the rear end of the body. (Fig. 601). Cuttlefish or little cuttle ....
..................................Order **Sepioida** (p. 117)

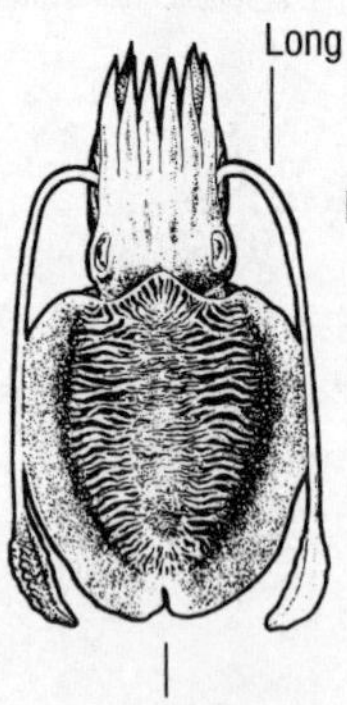

Long tentacle

Fig. 601

Gap between
lateral fins

–   The two tentacles are not much longer than the other 8 arms, and are not retractable into pits. The lateral fins meet at the rear end of the body, which may be extended into a long 'tail'. (Fig. 602). Squid
..............................Order **Teuthoida** (p. 117)

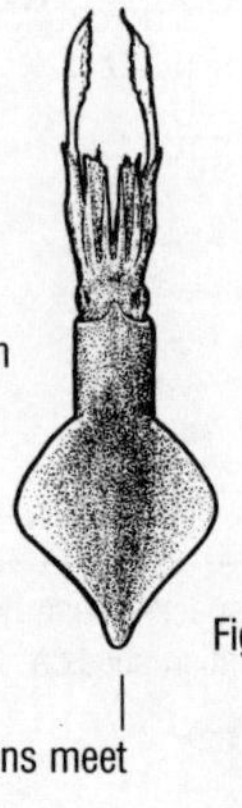

Fig. 602

Lateral fins meet

6:4 (6:2) – With an obvious opening (exhalant siphon) to the **mantle cavity** – which is hidden under the shell **6:5**

– Without a conspicuous exhalent siphon to the mantle cavity ....
.........................Subclass **Euthyneura** Super-Order **Opisthobranchia** **6:6**

6:5 (6:4) – Head, and all the rest of the body, covered by the **mantle**. Exhalent opening from the **mantle cavity**, faces forwards. The front edge of the foot is not divided or expanded into lobes. *Lamellaria* ....Subclass **Prosobranchia** Super-Order **Caenogastropoda** Order **Neotaenioglossa** (p. 110)

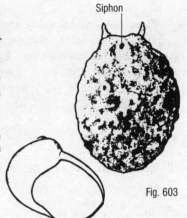

Siphon

Fig. 603

NOTE: Over the shell, the mantle bears tubercles and markings that mimic the appearance of tunicates, barnacles or sponges. (Fig. 603) Animal up to 20mm long x 12mm across; a predator of compound ascidians from low water mark down to 100m

– The mantle does not cover the head. Exhalent siphon from the mantle cavity faces backwards. The front edge of the foot is divided and expanded into two pedal lobes. (Fig. 604). *Colpodaspis pusilla* ....Subclass **Euthyneura** Super-Order **Opisthobranchia** Order **Cephalaspidea** (p. 111)

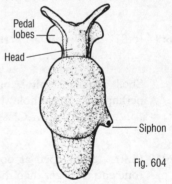

Pedal lobes

Head

Siphon

Fig. 604

6:6 (6:4) – Body shape quadripartite, that is it appears to be made up of 4 parts: cephalic lobe in the front, the mantle covering the dome shaped shell behind and a parapodium on either side. (Fig. 605). These parapodia, lateral extensions of the foot, cannot meet in the mid line and are not used for swimming ....Order **Cephalaspidea** Family **Philinidae** (p. 111)

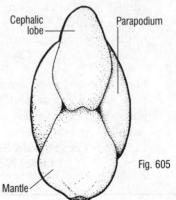

Cephalic lobe

Parapodium

Fig. 605

Mantle

– Body shape not quadripartite. Parapodia may meet in the mid-line and may be used for swimming **6:7**

6:7 (6:6) – Distinctive elongated sea slug with a conspicuous parapodial crest on top of the body; horseshoe- shaped, opening forwards. (Fig. 606). Sea hare ....Order **Anaspidea** Family **Aplysiidae** (p. 112)

NOTE: May reach 200mm in length. Herbivore. A pair of **rhinophores** behind the eyes look a bit like 'ears' and suggest the colloquial name

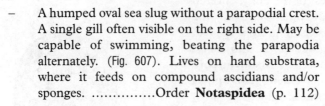

Parapodial crest

Fig. 606

– A humped oval sea slug without a parapodial crest. A single gill often visible on the right side. May be capable of swimming, beating the parapodia alternately. (Fig. 607). Lives on hard substrata, where it feeds on compound ascidians and/or sponges. ....Order **Notaspidea** (p. 112)

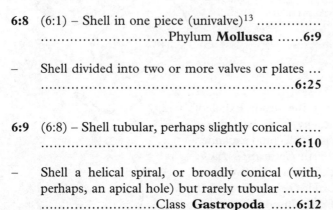

Fig. 607

6:8 (6:1) – Shell in one piece (univalve)[13] ....Phylum **Mollusca** **6:9**

– Shell divided into two or more valves or plates **6:25**

6:9 (6:8) – Shell tubular, perhaps slightly conical **6:10**

– Shell a helical spiral, or broadly conical (with, perhaps, an apical hole) but rarely tubular ....Class **Gastropoda** **6:12**

6:10 (6:9) – Shell open at both ends, slightly conical (one end is bigger than the other), smooth, slightly curved and often elongated: like a miniature elephant's tusk. Animal without a plate-like cover to the tube (operculum). Elephant's tusk shell ... .Class **Scaphopoda** **6:11**

– Shell a small (up to 4mm long), slightly curved, tube closed at one end by a domed or conical plate. (Fig. 608) May have conspicuous growth rings (annuli). Animal with an operculum. *Caecum* sp. ......Class **Gastropoda** Subclass **Prosobranchia** Order **Neotaenioglossa** (p. 110)

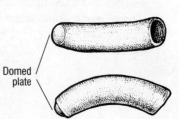

Domed plate

Fig. 608

---

[13] Look closely at a shell which appears to be all in one piece if the animal is firmly fixed to the substratum. In some bivalved shells the lower valve is cemented to the rock and is very difficult to see from above.

6:11 (6:10) – The animal has a substantial, spade-like burrowing foot (Fig. 609) and captures its prey with numerous thin prehensile tentacles (captaculae) ....Order **Dentalioidea** (p. 113)

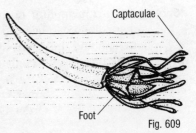

Captaculae

Foot

Fig. 609

– The animal has a long thread-like (**filiform**) foot that expands into a pedal disc at or near the end. It captures its prey with a few large, broad, captaculae ....Order **Siphonodentalioidea** (p. 113)

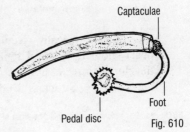

Captaculae

Pedal disc

Foot

Fig. 610

6:12 (6:9) – When the animal retracts into its shell, the aperture is more or less closed by a circular or ear-shaped horny plate (**operculum**), sometimes strengthened with calcareous matter **6:13**

– Operculum absent **6:18**

6:13 (6:12) – Look at the shell apex: the direction of shell coiling changes abruptly, through 90° or 180°, at the junction between the first-formed (**protoconch**) and later (**teloconch**) parts of the shell. The 'heterostrophic condition' (Fig. 611) ....Subclass **Heterobranchia** Order **Heterostropha** (p. 111)

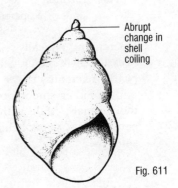

Abrupt change in shell coiling

Fig. 611

– Look at the shell apex: the direction of shell coiling does not change at the junction between protoconch and teloconch. The 'orthostrophic condition' **6:14**

6:14 (6:13) – Operculum horny, frail and elongated, amber coloured. The head shield (cephalic disc) is flattened and functions as a plough when the animal burrows through sand. (Fig. 612). *Acteon tornatilis* ....Subclass **Euthyneura**
Super-Order **Opisthobranchia**
Order **Cephalaspidea** (p. 111)

Fig. 612

NOTE: Shell up to 25mm in length, light pink in colour with 1-3 white bands on the body whorl and one on each of the other major whorl

– Operculum typically circular or ear-shaped (sub-oval) showing a spiral coiling pattern. Head not developed into a cephalic disc ....
.................Subclass **Prosobranchia** **6:15**

NOTE: Head has a distinct snout flanked by a pair of tentacles, with eyes at their base

6:15 (6:14) – Operculum circular. Shell with a mother of pearl (nacreous) inner layer (look inside the aperture) and either with a slit up the front (anterior) face of the shell or with the shell opening smooth in outline (Fig. 613). Male without a penis. Topshell ....Order **Vetigastropoda**
Superfamily **Trochacea** (p. 109)

Fig. 613

– Operculum typically ear-shaped (sub-oval) but occasionally circular. Shell without a mother-of -pearl (nacreous) layer and with the aperture outline either smooth or drawn out into one or more canals. Male with a large, and sometimes conspicuous, penis behind the head on his right side **6:16**

6:16 (6:15) – Aperture entire, typically rounded or ear-shaped (Fig. 614) ....
....................Order **Neotaenioglossa** (p. 110)

– The smooth line of the aperture lip is broken by one or more projections or canals **6:17**

Fig. 614

6:17 (6:16) – The shell aperture has an anterior siphonal groove (or tube) through which an inhalant siphon projects. Operculum ear-shaped. (Fig. 615). Whelk ....Order **Neogastropoda** (p. 110)

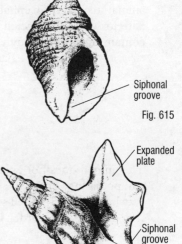

Siphonal groove

Fig. 615

– The outer lip of the shell's aperture is expanded into a plate shaped like the webbed foot of a bird. Operculum narrow and lying across the foot. (Fig. 616). Pelican's foot shell ....
...................................Order **Neotaenioglossa** Family **Aporrhaidae** (p. 110)

Expanded plate

Siphonal groove

Fig. 616

6:18 (6:12) – The sides of the foot are not expanded into great folds (**parapodia**) **6:19**

– The sides of the foot are expanded into great folds, (parapodia) which may be used for swimming and/or partly cover the shell when the animal is crawling ....Super-Order **Opisthobranchia** **6:20**

6:19 (6:18) – The head expanded into a head shield (cephalic disc) often with eyes clearly visible on top. Any head tentacles typically extend backwards from the posterior margin. If the front of the cephalic disc is divided to form two forward-facing points, the rear end of the foot is deeply notched. Shell too small to accommodate the animal during defensive contraction ....
.........Super-Order **Opisthobranchia** **6:20**

– Head not expanded as a cephalic disc. Eyes at the bases of the two, forward facing, head tentacles. Rear end of the foot not deeply notched ....
....**6:21**

6:20 (6.18) – The parapodia are large enough for the animal to swim. Cephalic disc slightly bilobed anteriorly. (Fig. 617). Shell delicate and too small to contain the whole body ....Order **Anaspidea**
Family **Akeridae** (p. 112)

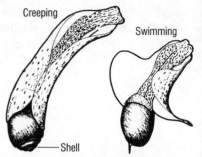

Creeping

Swimming

Shell

Fig. 617

– The animal does not normally swim although the parapodia may cover the shell when the animal is crawling. (Fig. 618). Shell solid and robust ....
........................Order **Cephalaspidea** (p. 111)

Fig. 618

6:21 (6:19) – Mantle cavity opens to the exterior through a muscular sphincter (the pneumostome), on the right side of the body behind the head. (Fig. 619). Land snail ....Subclass **Euthyneura**
Super-Order **Pulmonata** (p. 112)

Fig. 619

NOTE: Living high on the shore, on exposed coasts or salt marshes. Shell less than 5mm in length, spirally coiled, perhaps very elongated or with an expanded body whorl. Never with holes or slits

– Opening of the mantle cavity not constrained by a sphincter ......Subclass **Prosobranchia** **6:22**

6:22 (6:21) – Shell provided with one or more exhalant apertures; with a nacreous inner layer (look inside the aperture) and with the aperture entire apart from any slit up the leading face. The head bears two tentacles and there may be several other ones around the edge of the mantle. Male without a penis. (Fig. 620). A perforate limpet or an ormer ...
..................Super-Order **Archaeogastropoda**
Order **Vetigastropoda**
Superfamily **Fissurellacea** (p. 109)

Fig. 620

– Shell imperforate **6:23**

6:23 (6:22) – The empty shell has an internal shelf ......
................................Order **Neotaenioglossa**
Super-family **Calyptraeacea** (p. 110)

NOTE: It is either limpet-shaped (without any ribs) or kidney-shaped, (Fig. 421) in which case living individuals are attached to each other, in chains

– Shell without an internal shelf **6:24**

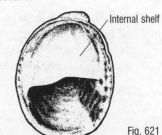

Internal shelf

Fig. 621

6:24 (6:22) – Shell broadly conical – limpet shaped – showing no sign of coiling. (Fig. 622). Limpet ......
.........Super-Order **Patellogastropoda** (p. 109)
or Super-Order **Archaeogastropoda**
Order **Cocculiniformia** p. 109)

Fig. 622

– Shell not limpet shaped or showing at least some traces of helical coiling. (Fig. 623) ....
.....................Order **Neotaenioglossa** (p. 110)

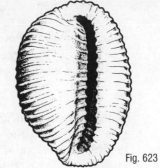
Fig. 623

6:25 (6:8) – Shell composed of eight, or more, valves or plates...**6:26**

– Shell essentially composed of two valves – left and right, or top and bottom (although there may be smaller accessory plates as well) **6:31**

6:26 (6:25) – Animal an elongate oval, flattened top-to-bottom (dorsoventrally), and bilaterally-symmetrical shape, having a dorsal shell composed of 8, transverse, serially-overlapping plates embedded in, and sometimes covered by, a girdle. Chiton ....Phylum **Mollusca**
Class **Polyplacophora** **6:27**

– Animal not typically an elongate oval in shape but, if so, the shell plates are not arranged in a row. Barnacle ....Phylum **Crustacea**
Class **Cirripedia** **6:29**

6:27 (6:26) – The girdle (area of skin around the edge of the chiton) encroaches over the shell valves, and typically bears tufts of bristles. (Fig. 624) ....Order **Acanthochitonina** (p. 108)

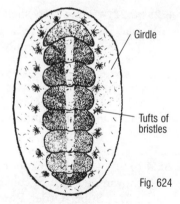

Girdle

Tufts of bristles

Fig. 624

\-   The girdle varies in width and extent, but does not encroach over the shell valves and never bears tufts of bristles **6:28**

6:28 (6:27) – When viewed from underside (under water) the gills are seen to occupy most of the pallial groove, except near the anus. [Left hand side of Fig. 625] ...Order **Ischnochitonina** (p.108)

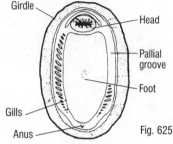

Girdle

Head

Pallial groove

Foot

Gills

Anus

Fig. 625

\-   When viewed from underside (under water) the gills only occupy the posterior end of the pallial groove, near the anus. [Right hand side of Fig. 625] ....Order **Lepidopleurina** (p.108)

6:29 (6:26) – The animal's body is hidden within (protected by) a series of calcareous plates ....Super-Order **Thoracica** **6:30**

\-   The animal's body is hidden within (protected by) the inside surface of an empty whelk shell occupied by a hermit crab. Presence of the burrowing barnacle is revealed by small dark slits visible in the shell's **columella**. (Fig. 626) ....Super-Order **Acrothoracica** (p. 124)

Slit in shell surface

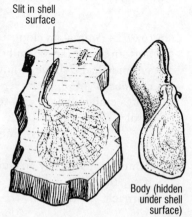

Body (hidden under shell surface)

Fig. 626

6:30 (6:29) – Some of the calcareous plates are typically fixed directly to the rock or to another firm surface (Fig. 627). Acorn barnacle ....
.................................Order **Sessilia** (p. 124)

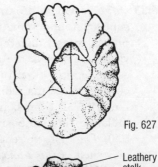

Fig. 627

– The calcareous plates are attached to a rock, floating object, or a self-secreted raft, by a tough leathery stalk. (Fig. 628). Stalked barnacle ....
.........................Order **Pedunculata** (p. 124)

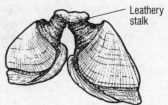

Leathery stalk

Fig. 628

6:31 (6:25) – Animal sedentary, firmly attached to (NOT burrowing within) the substratum. Strictly a bi-valved animal without accessory plates ....
....**6:32**

– Animal capable of at least some movement, perhaps free-living amongst lichens, or burrowing in mud, sand, clay or soft rocks. Perhaps even swimming. Body laterally-compressed and bilaterally-symmetrical, enclosed within two (left and right) calcareous shell valves, hinged by an elastic ligament and, typically, aligned with interlocking shell teeth. Perhaps (if burrowing in wood, clay or shale) with accessory plates in addition to the two valves proper. *It is necessary to have an empty shell available to proceed further in the key* ...Phylum **Mollusca** Class **Bivalvia** **6:43**

6:32 (6:31) – Lower valve of the shell is cemented to the rock **6:33**

– Neither valve is cemented to the rock, animal attached by threads (byssus) or by a stalk of some kind **6:34**

6:33 (6:32) – Up to 15mm long. In life, shell valves gape open and some 60 non-retractile filaments project in each antero-lateral crescent. When the valves are closed, the animal appears limpet-like, as the (entire) lower valve is invisible. Upper valve conical, wider than long, and without an obvious hinge line. It bears concentric growth lines but no radiating ribs: umbo not close to the hinge. (Fig. 629). Dark brown/reddish periostracum covers a grey shell. *Crania anomala* ....
.........Phylum **Brachiopoda** Class **Inarticulata**
Order **Acrotretida** (p. 118)

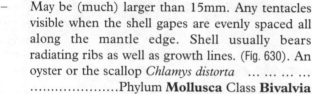

Fig. 629

– May be (much) larger than 15mm. Any tentacles visible when the shell gapes are evenly spaced all along the mantle edge. Shell usually bears radiating ribs as well as growth lines. (Fig. 630). An oyster or the scallop *Chlamys distorta* ... ...
....................Phylum **Mollusca** Class **Bivalvia**
Order **Ostreoida** (p. 115)

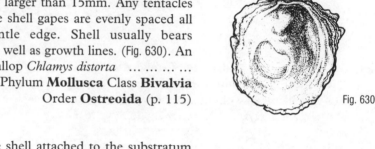

Fig. 630

6:34 (6:32) – Bivalve shell attached to the substratum by a leathery stalk ....Phylum **Brachiopoda**
Class **Articulata** **6:35**

– Bivalve shell attached to the substratum by a bunch of fine threads (byssus) ....
....................Phylum **Mollusca** Class **Bivalvia**
Super-Order **Lamellibranchia** **6.36**

6:35 (6:34) – Shell solid, not perforated by canals. (Fig. 631). Lophophore in the form of two spirally-coiled lobes, supported by spikes ....
.....................Order **Rhynchonellida** (p. 119)

Fig. 631

– Shell valves perforate, penetrated by canals: the openings of which are visible on the inside of the shell (Fig. 632). Lophophore in the form of two simple loops and a coiled central lobe supported by a loop ....Order **Terebratulida** (p. 119)

Fig. 632

6:36 (6:34) – The existence of the byssus is evident in the empty shell, which has a byssal aperture (hole through the lower valve) or a byssal notch. (Fig. 633). Saddle oyster ......Order **Ostreoida** (p. 115)

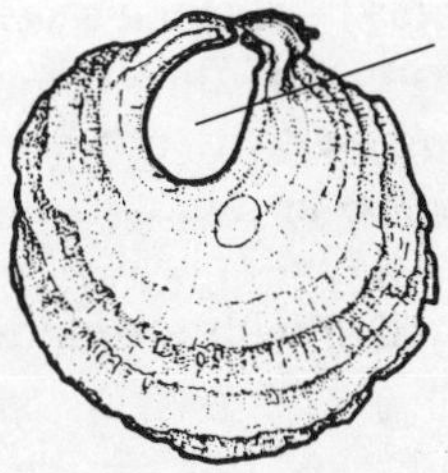

Byssal aperture

Lower valve

Fig. 633

– The empty shell is without a byssal notch or byssal aperture **6:37**

6:37 (6:36) – The two adductor muscles are of markedly different size so that the anterior end of the shell is very much smaller than the posterior, giving it a triangular appearance **6:38**

– A round, oval or rectangular shell **6:39**

6:38 (6:37) – An inhabitant of sub-littoral sandy or gravelly substrata. (Fig. 634). Wing oyster or fan mussel ....Order **Pterioida** (p. 114)

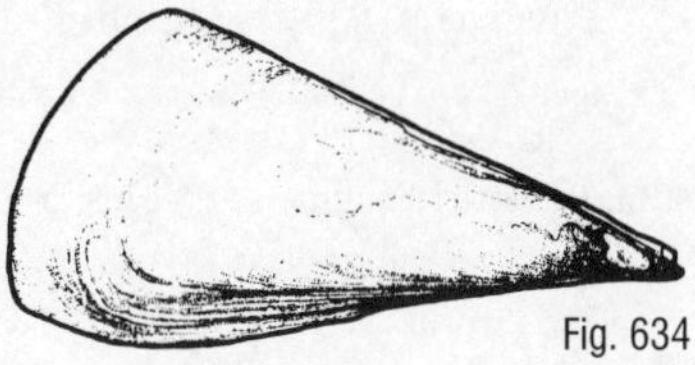

NOTE: Lives partially buried – attached to a stone by its byssus. Capable of reaching a very large size (300mm)

Fig. 634

– An inhabitant of intertidal or shallow sub-tidal rocky outcrops. (Fig. 635). Mussel ....
...............................Order **Mytiloida** (p. 114)

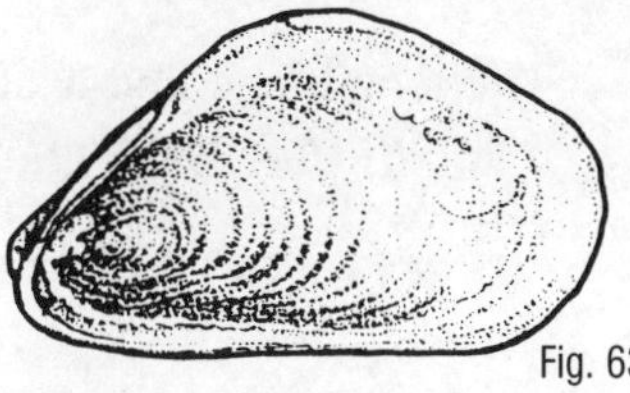

Fig. 635

6:39 (6:37) – A small, round shell, reddish in colour, found in the high intertidal within empty barnacle shells or amongst the lichen *Lichina pygmaea*. (Fig. 636). *Lasaea adansoni* ....
.......................Superfamily **Galeommatacea**
Order **Veneroida** (p. 115)

Fig. 636

– An oval, rhomboidal or rectangular shell **6:40**

6:40 (6:39) – A small rectangular shell, often somewhat distorted through living in eroded piddock burrows or other crevices. (Fig. 637). *Sphenia binghami* ....Order **Myoida** (p. 116)

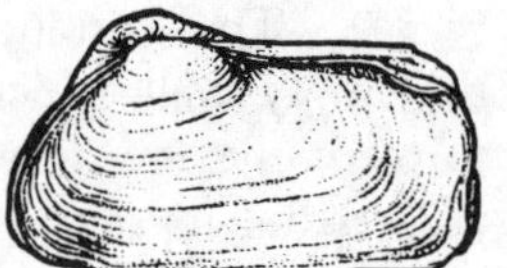

Fig. 637

– A shell with a rounded outline **6:41**

6:41 (6:40) – A rhomboidally shaped shell. (Fig. 638). Carpet shell ....Order **Veneroida** (p. 115)

NOTE: A solid shell, perhaps 40-50mm long. living in patches of muddy gravel on an otherwise rocky shore

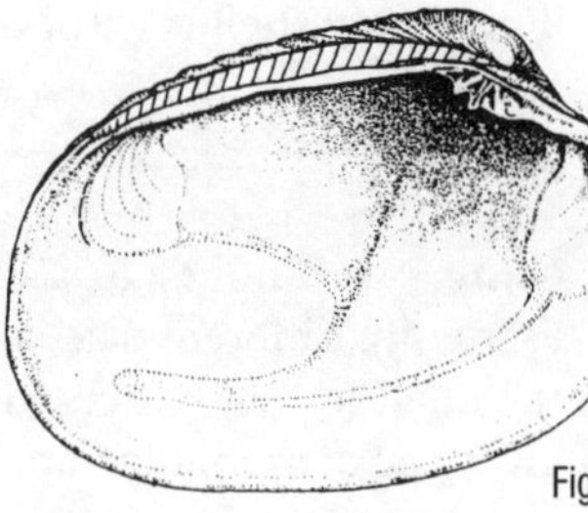

– An oval shell **6:42**

Fig. 638

6:42 (6:41)– The short hinge line is at one end of the oval (Fig. 639). File shell ....Order **Limoida** (p. 115)

NOTE: The edge of the mantle is fringed with long colourful flexible tentacles

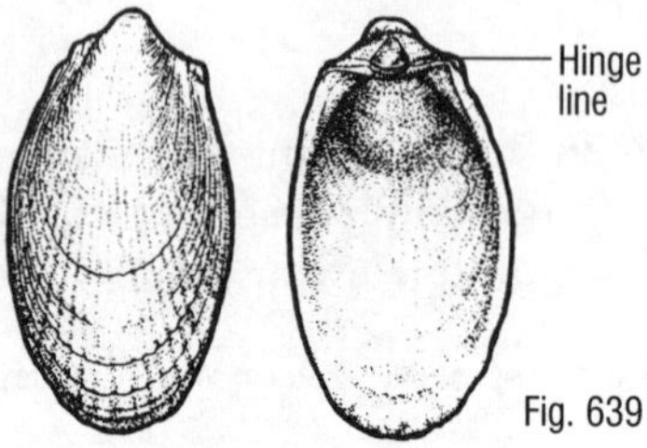

Hinge line

Fig. 639

– The long hinge line is along one side of the oval. (Fig. 640). *Galeomma turtoni* ....Order **Veneroida** (p.115)

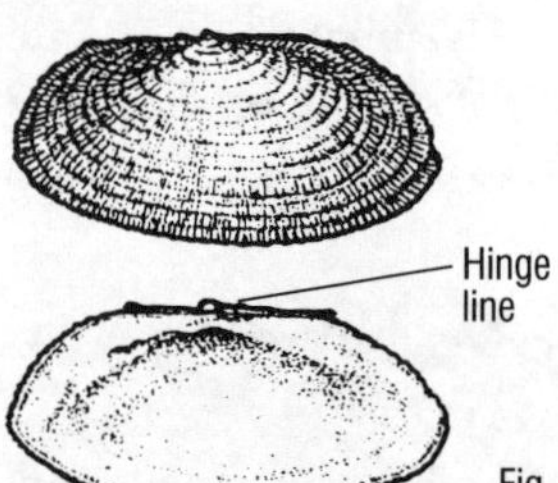

Hinge line

Fig. 640

6:43 (6:31) – The hinge between the two shell valves is taxodont – a long row of alternating teeth and sockets **6:44**

– Hinge not taxodont: there are either no hinge teeth at all, or there are a few pairs of dissimilar large teeth ....Super-Order **Lamellibranchia** **6:45**

6:44 (6:43) – Ligament internal in a small triangular pit and not visible in the living animal. Shell small (less than 20mm), smooth, white, equivalve and triangular-elliptical in shape. (Fig. 641). Nut shell ....Super-Order **Protobranchia** Order **Nuculoida** (p. 114)

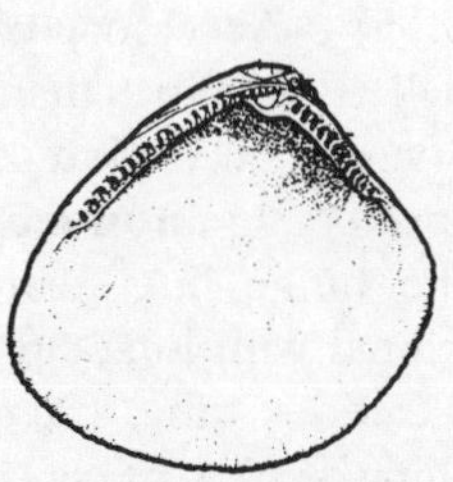

Fig. 641

– Ligament external. A thick, nearly circular equivalve shell (up to 64mm) that is nearly equilateral and bears fine concentric and transverse grooves. (Fig. 642) ....Super-Order **Lamellibranchia** Order **Arcoida** (p. 114)

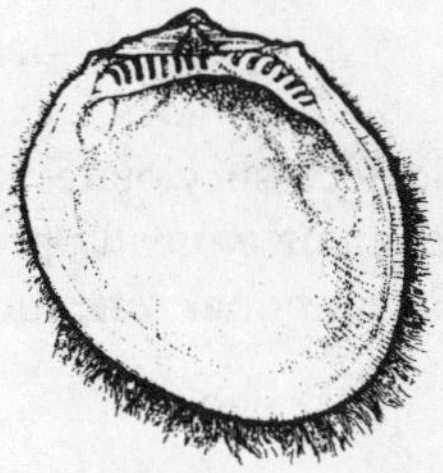

Fig. 642

6:45 (6:43) – The hinge line is drawn out, beside the umbones, into lateral projections (wings or ears – and not necessarily symmetrical). With a single adductor muscle scar. (Fig. 643). Scallop ....Order **Ostreoida** Superfamily **Pectinacea** (p. 115)

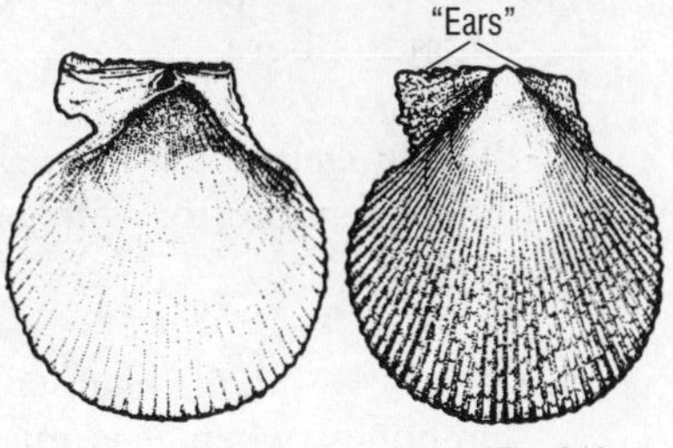

"Ears"

Fig. 643

– Without ears or wings, and with one, two (or, rarely, three) adductor muscle scars **6:46**

6:46 (6:45) – The posterior region of the shell is extended into a projecting spout. (Fig. 644) ....Family **Cuspidariidae** Super-Order **Septibranchia** Order **Poromyoida** (p. 117)

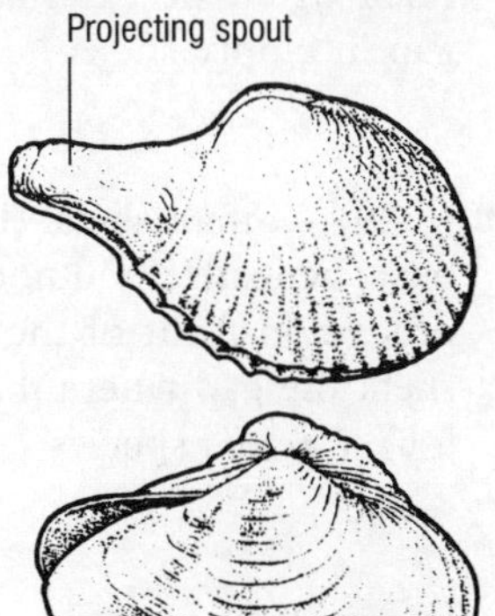

Projecting spout

Fig. 644

– Posterior region of the shell is not extended into a spout **6:47**

6:47 (6:45) – Accessory plates are developed: i.e., the shell is in more than two pieces. Shell ligament much reduced (and internal), typically attached to a projecting **chondrophore**. Without hinge teeth. The hinge line near the umbones is reflected. Animal with long siphons, perhaps protected by a calcareous tube. (Fig. 645). A burrower into wood (shipworm), stiff clay, or soft rock. Piddock ....
....Order **Myoida**
Superfamily **Pholadacea** (p. 116)

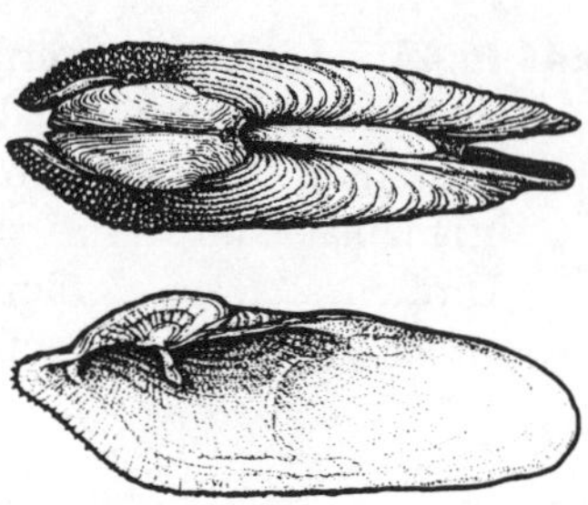

Fig. 645

– No accessory plates, the shell is truly bivalve. Shell ligament typically prominent (in a living animal). No umbonal reflection to the hinge line **6:48**

6:48 (6:47) – The hinge line is without teeth or chondrophore **6:49**

– The hingeline is armed either with teeth or with a chondrophore, or with both together **6:54**

6:49 (6:48) – Shell ligament internal, behind the umbones: when it is missing (in empty shells) it leaves a prominent gap **6:50**

– Shell ligament external. There is no prominent gap in empty shells **6:51**

6:50 (6:49) – Small shells (less than 4mm long) which bear, beneath the umbones, a crenulate tooth-like process in front of the ligament (or, in an empty shell, the gap where the ligament used to be) (Fig. 646). *Crenella* species ...Order **Mytiloida** (p. 113)

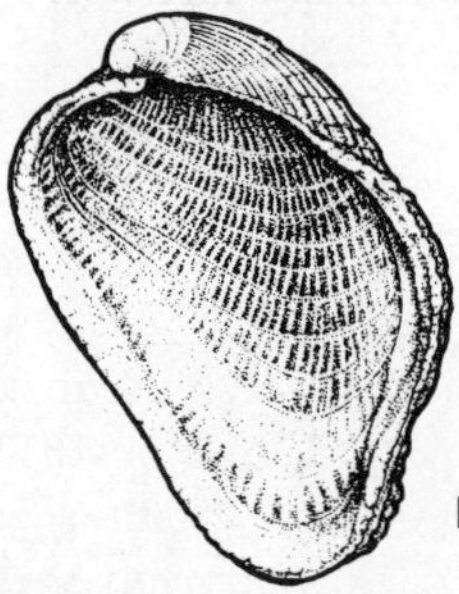

Fig. 646

– Up to about 13mm in length. Shells without a crenulate tooth-like process in front of the ligament. (Fig. 647) ....
........................Super-family **Galeommatacea**
Order **Veneroida** (p. 115)

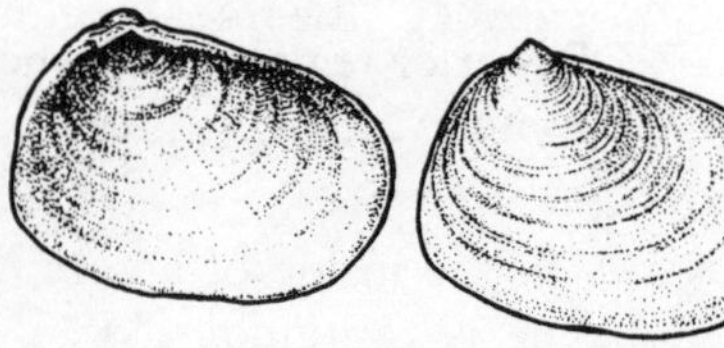

Fig. 647

6:51 (6:49) – Umbones at one (the anterior) end of the shell, or closer to it than they are to the mid line **6:52**

– Umbones closer to the mid-line than they are to either end. (Fig. 648) ....Family **Thyasiridae** Order **Veneroida** (p. 115)

NOTE: Muscle scars indistinct on the inside of empty shells

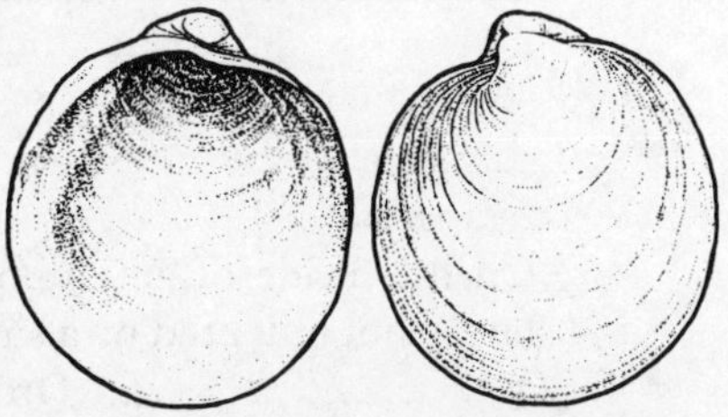

Fig. 648

6:52 (6:51) – Shell with a prominent anterior ventral gape **6:53**

– Shell without a prominent ventral gape (Fig. 649). Mussel ....Family **Mytilidae** Order **Mytiloida** (p. 114)

NOTE: The pallial line (on the inside of empty shells) without an indented sinus

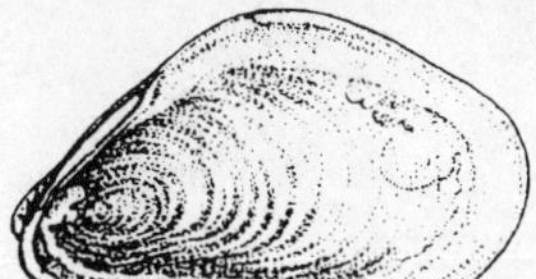

Fig. 649

6:53 (6:52) – A large (may exceed 300mm) fan-shaped shell, regularly triangular in outline (Fig. 650). Posterior adductor muscle scar nearly in the centre of each valve. *Pinna fragilis* fan mussel ....Order **Pterioida** (p. 114)

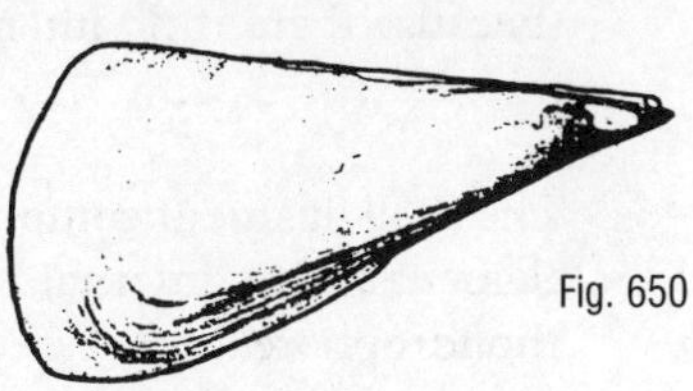

Fig. 650

– Typically less than 25mm, an irregularly triangular shell with the posterior adductor muscle scar near to the dorsal line (not in the centre of the valves) (Fig. 651). *Gastrochaena dubia* flask shell ....Order **Myoida** (p. 116)

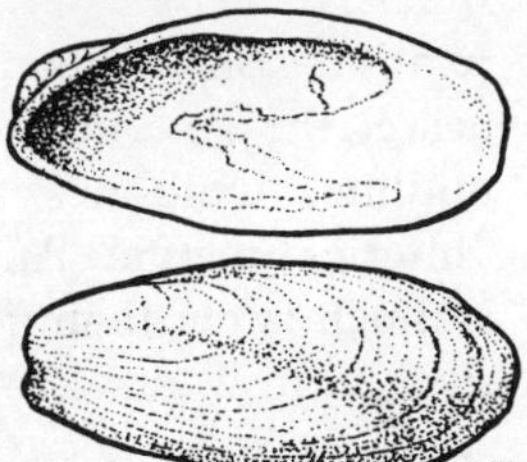

Fig. 651

6:54 (6:48) – On the inside of an empty shell valve, the **pallial line** is discontinuous; represented by a series of small separate muscle scars (Fig. 652). Shell inequivalve the right valve flat and the left convex. Ligament internal. *Pandora* spp – Pandora's box ...Order **Pholadomyoida** (p. 117)

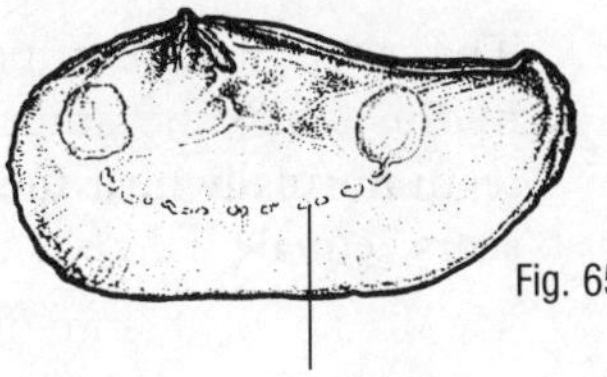

Fig. 652

Pallial line

– On the inside of an empty shell valve, the pallial line is continuous; or, if not, the shell is not as described above. Ligament may be internal, external, or both **6:55**

6:55 (6:53) – On the inside of an empty shell valve, the pallial line is indented by a sinus (Fig. 653) – although this may not be as large as in the illustration **6:56**

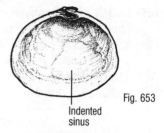

Fig. 653

Indented
sinus

– On the inside of an empty shell valve, the pallial line is not indented by a sinus (Fig. 654) ....
..............................Order **Veneroida** (p. 115)

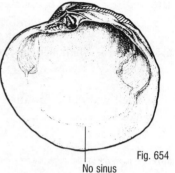

Fig. 654

No sinus

6:56 (6:55) – The shell ligament wholly external, although, possibly, deeply inset. No chondrophore (because there is no internal element) ....
....**6:57**

– The shell ligament comprises external and internal elements: the internal element anchored in a chondrophore **6:59**

6:57 (6:56) – Shell ligament beginning and ending nearer the anterior margin of the shell than the midline. Umbones and teeth near the front (anterior) margin. Anterior adductor muscle scar is much larger than the posterior (Fig. 655). Razor shell ....Order **Myoida** (p. 116)

Fig. 655

NOTE: Shell an elongate rectangle in outline, 4 or 5 times as long as deep

– The shell ligament begins or ends nearer the midline than the anterior margin. Umbones and teeth normally near the midline. Adductor muscle scars equal **6:58**

6:58 (6:57) – On the inside of one valve there is a single **cardinal tooth**: the other has either 2 or none – and all teeth may be worn away! The pallial line may be represented by a series of disconnected muscle scars (Fig. 656) ......Order **Myoida** (p. 116)

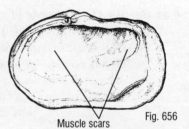

Muscle scars   Fig. 656

–   On the inside of an empty shell, each valve always has more than one cardinal tooth. The pallial line is always complete (Fig. 657) ....
...............................Order **Veneroida** (p. 115)

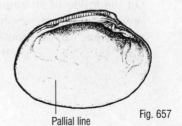

Pallial line   Fig. 657

6:59 (6:56) – Shell with the right valve very much larger than the left with a curtain of the larger valve's periostracum enclosing the exposed part of the smaller valve. Ligament internal (Fig. 658). Up to 12.7mm long. *Corbula gibba* basket shell ....
...................................Order **Myoida** (p. 116)

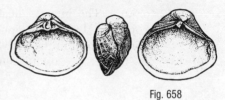

Fig. 658

–   Shell more or less equivalve, ligament may be internal or external **6:60**

6:60 (6:59) – On the inside of an empty shell valve, there is/are one or more cardinal teeth **6:61**

–   On the inside of an empty shell valve, there are no cardinal teeth **6:62**

6:61 (6:60) – On the inside of an empty shell valve, the pallial sinus is but a small indentation. The right valve has one cardinal tooth and no laterals whilst the left has one lateral tooth and no cardinals (Fig. 659). *Poromya granulata* ....
...........................Super-Order **Septibranchia**
Order **Poromyoida** (p. 117)

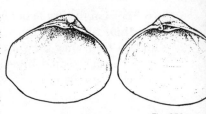

Fig. 659

– On the inside of an empty shell valve, the pallial sinus is a prominent indentation. Both valves have at least one cardinal tooth (Fig. 660) ....
...............................Order **Veneroida** (p. 116)

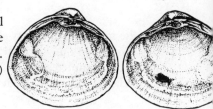

Fig. 660

6:62 (6:60) – The internal ligament is attached to a projecting spoon-shaped structure (the chondrophore) in the left valve (Fig. 661). Clam ...
..................................Order **Myoida** (p. 116)

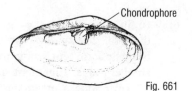

Chondrophore

Fig. 661

– On the inside of an empty shell, there is no projecting spoon-shaped chondrophore in the left valve (Fig. 662). The internal ligament is attached to various pits below and about the umbones ....
.....................Order **Pholadomyoida** (p. 116)

Fig. 662

KEY 7

A KEY TO WORMS

All the keys were written for field biologists with, on occasion, limited laboratory support in the way of binocular microscopes, and the assumption is made that the specimen is alive, and is being viewed under sea water, unless some comment is made to the contrary. **Bold type** in the text indicates terms that are defined in the glossary (p. 144).

7:1 – A disc-shaped ectoparasite of a feather star or a sponge, not much longer than broad **7:2**

– A free-living worm, or with a body much longer than broad **7:3**

7:2 (7:1) A worm (>4mm in length) parasitic on the feather star, *Antedon bifida* (p. 138), yellow / brown in colour. Somitation inconspicuous except that the almost circular body has 10 pairs of marginal cirri (Fig. 701). *Myzostoma cirriferum* ....
....Phylum **Annelida**
Class **Myzostomata** (p. 105)

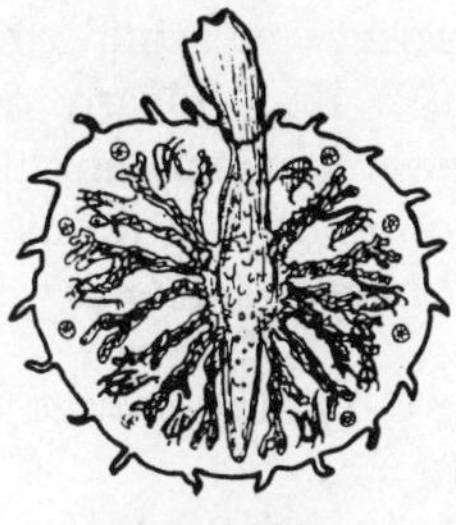

Fig. 701

– A worm (>28mm in length) associated with a sponge. Colour depends on the host colour. Somitation apparent and with 12 or more somites (Fig. 702). *Spinther* ....Phylum **Annelida**
Class **Polychaeta**
Order **Spintherida** (p. 103)

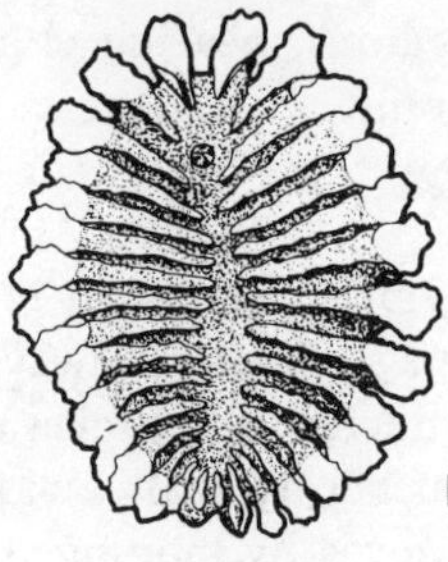

Fig. 702

7:3 (7:2) – The body appears to be formed of a series of replicated **somites**[14] [perhaps only visible on the under (ventral) side], which may bear bristles or other outgrowths. The head may bear jaws or be adorned with a crown of tentacles ...**7:4**

– Body apparently unsomited (not formed of a long series of replicated somites), even on the ventral side, although it may be divided into a few discrete regions **7:24**

---

[14] Segment. There is confusion of terminology in the literature. Some authors use the word 'segment' for the body somites of, for example, a worm or a shrimp. Others use it for the sections of arthropod appendages. I have tried to follow the latter convention and use "somite" for the replicated sections of the body.

7:4 (7:3) – Thirteen (or fewer) somites, which are typically (but not always) at least as long as they are broad. With or withour prolegs. Body not covered with a series of overlapping scales, without tentacles or bristles and without a sucker at each end. (Fig. 703). Fly larva ....
...............................Sub-Phylum **Atelocerata**
Class **Hexapoda**
probably Order **Diptera** (p. 135)

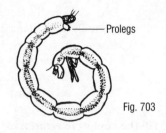

Fig. 703

– Fourteen (or more – typically very many more) somites which are usually (but not always) broader than they are long. Without prolegs. Perhaps, the body is covered with pairs of overlapping scales or have a sucker at each end **7:5**

7:5 (7:4) – With bunches of structures that look like brushes or 'ants' eggs' at the posterior end (Fig. 704). Body clearly divided into two regions and covered in an annulated (animal is not actually somited) chitinous cuticle. Without chaetae. *Priapulus caudatus* ......Phylum **Priapula** (p. 96)

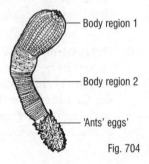

Fig. 704

NOTE: Uses proboscis for burrowing. Up to 75 mm long

– Body without 'ants' eggs' and, if divided into two regions, bearing clumps of chaetae on almost all somites ....Phylum **Annelida** **7:6**

7:6 (7:5) – Animal an ectoparasite of a fish – although may be found away from its host – to which it attaches by a sucker at both ends of its body. Head sucker typically wider than the body (Fig. 705). Moves by looping. Leech ....Class **Clitellata**
Subclass **Hirudinoida**
Order **Rhynchobdellida** (p. 106)

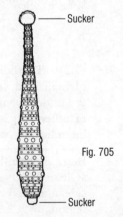

Fig. 705

– Without a sucker at each end of the body. Does not move by looping **7:7**

7:7 (7:6) – Small (less than 20mm long) and extremely thin (length 30x to 60x width) worm, pointed at both ends (Fig. 706). Head without tentacles or jaws. Body somites with few or no chaetae but (when adult) with a glandular area of skin (the **clitellum**) near the head end which secretes the cocoon ....Class **Clitellata**
Subclass **Oligochaeta**
Order **Haplotaxida** (p. 105)

Fig. 706

– Often (much) more than 20mm long. Never with a clitellum. Head may bear jaws or tentacles or both. Chaetae typically abundant and often borne on fleshy outgrowths of the body wall (parapodia) ....Class **Polychaeta** **7:8**

7:8 (7:7) The worm is an active hunting animal. It may burrow but does not live in a permanent tube attached to the substrate **7:9**

– The worm is a passive feeder, living in a more-or-less permanent tube or burrow and feeding on material that settles from the water column ....
....**7:10**

7:9 (7:8) The worm is living in a tube which it carries about with it **7:11**

– The worm is free-living **7:12**

7:10 (7:8) – The worm's tube is not attached to the substrate but is carried about by the worm ....
....**7:11**

– The worm lives in a burrow or in a tube permanently fixed to or in the substrate. The worm is incapable of moving its tube from place to place although it can repair damage if necessary
....**7:17**

7:11 (7:9 or 7:10) – The tube is flexible – really a mucous sheath (perhaps encrusted with sand or mud grains) through which the chaetae project and enable the worm to move around, slowly. (Fig. 707). Perhaps commensal with a sea urchin. The worms have green blood so their gills are green and not red ....Order **Flabelligerida** (p. 104)

Fig. 707

– The tube is rigid and composed of sand grains cemented together. It is approximately circular in cross section, perhaps slightly curved in outline and expanding in diameter towards the head end of the worm (Fig. 708). The worm lives in sand with the small end of the tube projecting above the surface ....Order **Terebellida** Family **Pectinariidae** (p. 105)

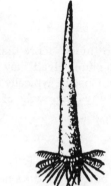

Fig. 708

7:12 (7:9): A short, rather fat, worm in which the small head appears to be sunk back behind the first pair of parapodia. Behind the head, a low fleshy crest (**caruncle**) extends backwards over the next few somites (Fig. 709). The two members of each pair of parapodia are widely separated, so that the dorsal member is on the upper body surface and there is an obvious gap between it and the lower member ....Order **Amphinomida** (p. 103)

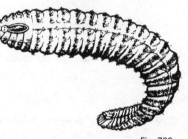

Fig. 709

– The head projects forward of the first pair of parapodia. There is no caruncle. The two members of each pair of parapodia are close together **7:13**

7:13 (7:12) – The dorsal surface of the worm is covered with overlapping scales (Fig. 710) or a felt of chaetae, so that the somites are only visible from the lower (ventral) side. Scale worm or sea mouse ....Order **Phyllodocida** Family **Aphroditidae** (p. 103)

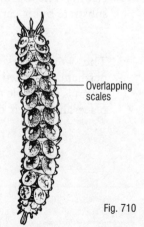

Overlapping scales

Fig. 710

– The body somites are visible in dorsal view ...**7:14**

7:14 (7:13) – A small, active, delicate worm with an obvious head bearing an odd number (probably 3) of head tentacles – one being central. Each somite down the body bears a pair of, often long and colourless, dorsal tentacles (cirri). (Fig. 711) ......
.....................................Order **Phyllodocida**
Family **Syllidae** (p. 103)

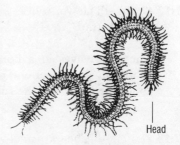

Head

Fig. 711

– The worm does not have all those extra tentacles along its body and, if it has head tentacles there are an even number **7:15**

7:15 (7:14) – A transparent free-living (pelagic) worm. A long head tentacle reaches more than halfway down each side of the body. (Fig. 712) ....
.....................................Order **Phyllodocida**
Family **Tomopteridae** (p. 103)

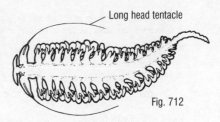

Long head tentacle

Fig. 712

NOTE: The parapodia bear swimming paddles

– A bottom-living (benthic) worm and, if found swimming, coloured and without head tentacles of the kind illustrated in Fig. 712 ....**7:16**

7:16 (7:15) – When pressed gently behind the head, the worm eventually rolls out (everts) a proboscis armed with jaws (perhaps for a surprisingly long distance in front of the head: Fig. 713). Probably, the worm has an obvious head with eyes and antennae ....Order **Phyllodocida**[15] (p. 103)

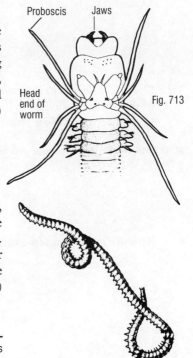

Proboscis   Jaws

Head end of worm

Fig. 713

– The worm is without a proboscis of this type, although it may have a retractable jaw structure (almost always invisible in the living worm). Probably, the head lacks eyes or antennae (or both) and it may be difficult to decide which is the front end (Fig. 714) ......Order **Eunicida** (p. 103)

[15] This is such a large Order (the British fauna is classified in 11 superfamilies comprising 28 families) that it is impossible to draw a composite figure and your specimen may not look much like the illustration.

Fig. 714

7:17 (7:10) – The worm lives in a tube *on the surface of* the substrate **7:18**

–   The worm lives in a burrow or in tube *in* the substrate. The upper end of that tube may project above the surface of the substrate **7:19**

7:18 (7:17) – The worm lives in a hard, white calcareous tube firmly attached to the surface of a rock, shell, seaweed etc. (Fig. 715) ....
..............................Order **Sabellida** (p. 105)
Families **Serpulidae** & **Spirorbidae**

NOTE: It closes the aperture of its tube with an operculum. When feeding, the operculum is pushed well clear of the aperture and feathery tentacles are extended into the water

Fig. 715

–   The worm lives in a tube composed of sand or mud grains ....Order **Terebellida** (p. 105)

NOTE: Perhaps the tube is firmly attached to rocks (perhaps many of them are cemented together and form a reef or a colony resembling a honeycomb: Fig. 716), family Sabellariidae. Or, perhaps, the tube is a fragile structure lying on the surface of the substrate, poorly attached, family Ampharetidae

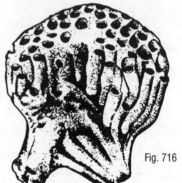

Fig. 716

7:19 (7:17) – The worm burrows into rock (limestone) or the shells of molluscs. (Fig. 717) ....
......Order **Spionida** Family **Spionidae** (p. 103)

NOTE: The head has two conspicuous palps which have a tendency to coil when the worm is disturbed

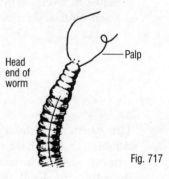

Head end of worm

Palp

Fig. 717

–   The worm burrows in sand or mud **7:20**

7:20 (7:19) – Without head or body tentacles. (Fig. 718).
Lug-worm ....Order **Capitellida**
Family **Arenicolidae** (p. 104)

NOTE: The worm bears chaetae on most somites and may bear (usually red) gills on some somites. Perhaps living in a U-shaped burrow in the sand, with a hollow forming over the head and a worm cast over the tail

– The worm bears tentacles (or palps or whatever) on the head and/or along the length of the body ...
....**7:21**

7:21 (7:20) – All tentacles and gills (which may be branched and feathery structures) are confined to the head and the first few somites behind it – or the extreme tail **7:22**

– The simple conical head is without tentacles but threadlike red gills (which writhe like tentacles) arise from many somites down the body. (Fig. 719).
...Order **Spionida** Family **Cirratulidae** (p. 103)

NOTE: Parapodia much reduced

7:22 (7:21) – Head with two palps or tentacles[16]. (Fig. 720) ....Order **Spionida** (p. 103)

– Head with more than two tentacles (probably many more) although they may grouped in two bunches **7:23**

---

[16] There are several other Orders comprising tiny interstitial worms that would key out here. See Westheide (1991).

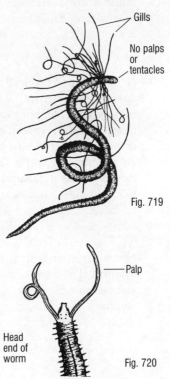

Fig. 717

Gills

No palps or tentacles

Fig. 719

Palp

Head end of worm

Fig. 720

7:23 (7:22) – The head bears a cluster of long mobile, probably colourless, tentacles (which continue to writhe about when broken off from the worm (Fig. 721) ....Order **Terebellida** (p. 105)

NOTE: Perhaps there are two or three pairs of red gills. The tapering body is divided into discrete regions so that the front 17 (or so) somites are more swollen than the many more that follow them

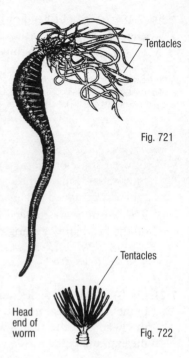

Tentacles

Fig. 721

Tentacles

Head end of worm

Fig. 722

– The head bears a crown of tentacles which, when extended, form a funnel shaped array. (Fig. 722). Some crowns are much more complicated than others. Fan worm ....
...............................Order **Sabellida** (p. 105)

7:24 (7:3) – A small (typically less than 20mm) very flat unsomited worm which glides over the substratum. The body does not necessarily change shape whilst moving. The sides of the body sweep down to touch the substrate without any intervening ridge (Fig. 723, Fig. 724). The common mouth / anus is positioned on the lower (ventral) side. No gills. Flatworm ....
...............................Phylum **Platyhelminthes**
                    Class **Turbellaria** **7:25**

– Not a *very* flat worm, perhaps the body is more cylindrical in form and it may change shape as the animal moves. The animal does not have a common mouth/anus on the lower (ventral) side
....**7:26**

7:25 (7:24) – An (often high) intertidal flatworm, about six times longer than broad, with a single pair of eyes. Front of the head rounded, or (in *Procerodes*, Fig. 723) with stubby marginal tentacles (like ears) but never with **nuchal tentacles** arising from the upper surface. Up to 11mm in length ....
.............................Order **Tricladida** (p. 90)

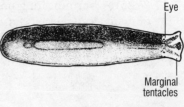

Fig. 723

– A lower shore or subtidal flatworm, not more than four times longer than broad, with many eyes, typically arranged in clusters (Fig. 724). Front of the head rounded, perhaps with two marginal tentacles: with, or without, **nuchal tentacles** arising from the upper surface (Fig. 724). Up to 40mm in length ....
.............................Order **Polycladida** (p. 90)

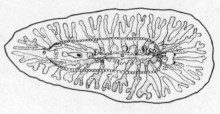

Fig. 724

7:26 (7:24) – Body with bunches of 'bottle-brushes' or 'ants' eggs' at the posterior end and covered in an annulated chitinous cuticle. *Priapulus caudatus* (Fig. 725) ....Phylum **Priapula** (p. 96)

NOTE: Body clearly divided into two regions. Uses proboscis for burrowing. Up to 75 mm long

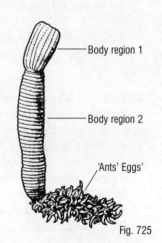

Fig. 725

– Body without bunches of 'bottle-brushes / ants' eggs' at the rear end, and without an annulated chitinous cuticle **7:27**

7:27 (7:26) – Worm bearing one or two pairs of lateral fins and a caudal (tail) fin. Arrow worm (Fig. 726)…
………………Phylum **Chaetognatha** (p. 136)

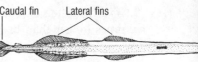

Caudal fin   Lateral fins

Fig. 726

NOTE: Apparently rigid – movement is by sudden flicks of the body – transparent or opaque worms, up to 90mm in length (but typically around 20mm). Typically planktonic but there is one benthic species in British waters

–   The worm does not bear lateral or caudal fins …
…………………………………………………………**7:28**

7:28 (7:27) – An elongated cylindrical 'worm', of uniform diameter, without a head or tail, which writhes purposelessly about, at the bottom of a petri dish, without progressing and without changing its length. Typically colourless, but may be pink ……………………………………………
    A detached tentacle of an annelid, probably from a cirratulid, Order **Spionida** or from a terrebellid, Order **Terebellida** (p. 105)

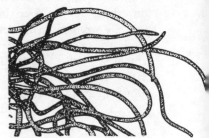

Fig. 727

–   The worm has an obvious head end, and/or does not writhe …………………………………………**7:29**

7:29 (7:28) – A small (typically 1-2mm but sometimes larger) cylindrical worm, typically pointed at both ends (although with a definite head) and frequently white in colour (Fig. 728). Never with lines of 'tube feet' along the body. Unable to alter its body length, although it may readily coil and uncoil its body. Never extends a crown of tentacles, or a proboscis, from one end of the body. Round worm …………………………Phylum **Nematoda** (p. 98)

Fig. 728

–   The worm (typically much longer than 2mm) is able to expand and contract its body and may produce a crown of tentacles from one end …**7:30**

7:30 (7:29) – The animal has tentacles on its head, and permanently visible, or perhaps it (eventually) everts a 'crown' of tentacles from one end of the body when at rest …………………………………**7:31**

–   The animal is without tentacles although it perhaps (eventually) everts a proboscis, or other structure, with finger-like growths around the oral disc which surrounds the mouth ……………**7:38**

7:31 (7:30) – The simple, unbranched, tentacles (of the lophophore) growing out of the front end are arranged in a horseshoe shape, with the mouth inside the ring and the anus outside (this is difficult to see). (Fig. 729) ....
...............................Phylum **Phorona** (p. 118)

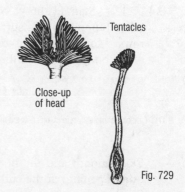

Tentacles

Close-up
of head

Fig. 729

NOTE: Animal living in a tube set vertically in the mud, or burrowed into calcareous rock / shells or encrusting a hard object

– The tentacles are not arranged in a horseshoe-shaped lophophore and the anus (if present) is not at the same end of the body as the mouth **7:32**

7:32 (7:31) – A very long, threadlike, 'worm' bearing between 1 and 7 very long ciliated tentacles on the cephalic lobe. There is no mouth, alimentary canal or anus ....Phylum **Pogonophora**
Class **Frenulatea** **7:33**

– The worm is not threadlike. There are no very long ciliated tentacles; but it does have an alimentary system **7:34**

7:33 (7:32) – With a single tentacle (Fig. 730), or with 7 tentacles ....Order **Athecanephrida** (p. 101)

– With 2, 3 or 4 tentacles ....
.....................Order **Thecanephridia** (p. 101)

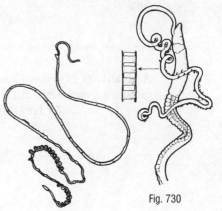

Fig. 730

7:34 (7:32)– Skin leathery, often with tubercles and other bumps on the surface perhaps arranged in rows. Mouth and anus terminal at opposite ends of the body. Sea cucumber ....
..............................Phylum **Echinodermata**
Class **Holothuroidea** **7:35**

NOTE: Tentacles completely retractable, only extended when the animal is relaxed (this may take hours!)

–   Skin smooth and the body lacks an anus (or any other opening) at the end away from the tentacles. Sea anemone ....Phylum **Cnidaria**
Sub-Phylum **Anthozoa**
Class **Hexacorallia** **7:37**

7:35 (7:34) – A truly worm-like animal with 11 or 12 tentacles, but with no tube feet or gills (respiratory trees).......................Order **Apodida** (p. 140)

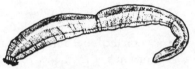

Fig. 731

–   A sausage-shaped animal that may have more than 12 tentacles (range 10-30) and with definite rows of tube feet along the body **7:36**

7:36 (7:35) – Animal with between 15 and 30 shield-shaped tentacles ....
.....................Order **Aspidochirotida** (p. 140)

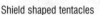

Shield shaped tentacles

Fig. 732

NOTE: Only the ventral rows of tube feet are locomotory

–   Animal with between 10 and 30 highly branched retractile tentacles ....
.....................Order **Dendrochirotida** (p. 140)

Fig. 733

7:37 (7:34) – A sea anemone with two series of tentacles; a short labial series arising from the mouth and a long marginal series arising from the periphery of the disc (Fig. 734). Lives in a tube buried in a soft substratum ....Order **Ceriantharia** (p. 87)

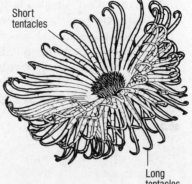

Short tentacles

Long tentacles

Fig. 734

– A sea anemone with a single series of tentacles, all arising from the periphery of the disc (Fig. 735), although there may be several whorls ....Order **Actiniaria** (p.87)

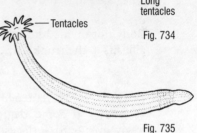

Tentacles

Fig. 735

7:38 (7:30) – The body is encased in a chitinous cuticle covered with calcareous spicules which may appear as scales or spines in different parts of the body ....Phylum **Mollusca** **7:39**

– The soft body is not covered with calcareous spicule **7:40**

7:39 (7:38) – Body with a conspicuous furrow down the ventral side, linking the mouth and the anus. Gills, when present, developed as folds. Mouth without a foot-shield ....Class **Solenogastres** (p. 107)

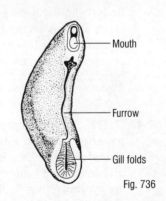

Mouth

Furrow

Gill folds

Fig. 736

– Body without a ventral furrow. and with a pair of gills (each divided into two lamellae) emerging from the anal cavity at the posterior end. Mouth surrounded by a foot shield. ....Class **Caudofoveata** (p. 107)

Fig. 737

NOTE: An inactive specimen looks a bit like a peculiar sponge [Phylum Porifera p. 90]

7:40 (7:38) – Body divided into three regions – (a) long proboscis, (b), short collar (which, ventrally, bears the mouth) and (c) a very long trunk. (Fig. 738). The trunk bears many 'pharyngeal gill slits', new ones being produced throughout life. Acorn worm ....Phylum **Hemichordata** Class **Enteropneusta** (p. 137)

NOTE: Whole animal can reach 3m in length

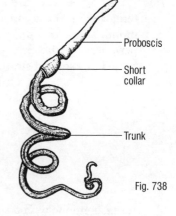

Proboscis

Short collar

Trunk

Fig. 738

 – Body not divided into three sections and without gill slits in the trunk **7:41**

7:41 (7:40) – Body flattened top-to-bottom (dorso-ventrally) to some degree; often moving quite freely over hard surfaces. With an obvious head-end, typically with eyes. If about 10mm long, perhaps moving by some sort of ciliary gliding but typically by (very obvious) waves of muscular contraction passing along the body. Body may be enormously extensible – up to many metres (Fig. 739). Ribbon worm ....Phylum **Nemertea** (p. 92)

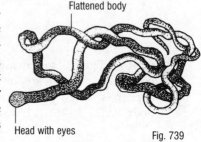

Flattened body

Head with eyes

Fig. 739

 – Body cylindrical or globular. An inactive animal living in sand or mud which (eventually) extends an enormous introvert from its front end. No head or eyes. Never moving by dramatic muscular contractions **7:42**

7.42 (7:41) – With a plump body, having an anus at the posterior end and a long proboscis which can be extended from the anterior mouth. (Fig. 740). The proboscis has a groove along its ventral side. There are typically two hooked chaetae on the ventral surface behind the mouth ....Phylum **Echiura** (p. 101)

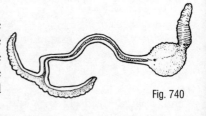

Fig. 740

 – With a cylindrical body, having an anus on the dorsal side towards the anterior end. (Fig. 741). The long introvert, which can be extended from the anterior end of the trunk, bears the mouth at its end. There is no groove along its ventral side. Never with chaetae ....Phylum **Sipuncula** (p. 100)

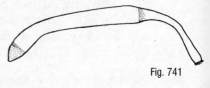

Fig. 741

CONFIRMATORY NOTES

Phylum PLACOZOA

Trichoplax adhaerens, known from various marine aquaria for over a century, was assumed to be the planuloid larva of some unknown marine invertebrate. As it has never shown any sign of developing into anything else, this phylum was erected to house it. Superficially similar to a giant amoeba (it reaches 3mm in diameter), the body is composed of about 1,000 cells in the form of a flattened disc of variable outline. The amoeboid similarity is continued in the way the body changes shape whilst crawling across the substratum. No organs or distinct tissues are present. Feeding is through extracellular digestion, from enzymes secreted from the lower surface of the body. Reproduction is by asexual fission and sexually-produced gametes.

Phylum PORIFERA

Sponges are sessile organisms, lacking distinct tissues and organs; muscular and nervous systems. All are benthic filter feeders. Except in the larval stage, they are incapable of movement. Although fundamentally bilaterally symmetrical, the sponge body often appears to be without symmetry (only a few species attain a characteristic shape). Its external surface is perforated by a large number of small inhalant openings (ostia) and one, or more, large exhalant tubes (oscula). Internally, the sponge body takes the form of a series of canals and chambers supported by an immovable skeletal matrix of calcareous and/or siliceous spicules, and/or organic spongin fibres. Water is drawn through the canals and chambers of the aquiferous system by the beating of the choanocyte cell flagella, lining the walls. These choanocytes are almost identical to free-living protoctistan Choanoflagellates. Most sponges are hermaphrodite, but not necessarily simultaneously. Spermatozoa leave and enter sponges via the aquiferous system. Fertilisation and embryogenesis take place within the sponge body, and short-lived ciliated larvae are released into the exhalant current. Metamorphosis rapidly follows settlement.

Sponges are easily recognised as such[17] but are renowned for being particularly difficult to identify to species. Traditionally, the skeletal spicules have been considered most important in classification. In calcareous sponges, these are all of much the same size, but in other groups they can be differentiated into larger megascleres and smaller microscleres. Spicule descriptions are based on the number of points; monactines are rod-like with one pointed end; diactines, rod-like with both ends pointed; three-rayed triactines; four-rayed tetractines etc. Four Classes are recognised but there are no British species in the Sclerospongiae, and no shallow water species of Hexactinellida. See Ackers, Moss, Picton & Stone (1985): Hayward & Ryland (1990; 1995).

---

[17] Although it might be possible for an inexperienced taxonomist to confuse an inactive caudofoveate mollusc for a sponge.

Class Calcarea

Marine sponges with a mineral skeleton composed entirely of calcium carbonate. The skeletal spicules, of calcite or aragonite and either free or secondarily fused, show a variety of shapes – mostly 3 or 4 rayed – but are not differentiated into megascleres and microscleres. There is still doubt regarding how many of the 'named forms' represent true species. The British fauna probably numbers somewhere between the 31 'named forms' and 7 'species', in 7 families. See Ackers, Moss, Picton & Stone (1985).

Subclass Calcinea

Any triactine spicules present have rays of equal length, set at approximately equal angles.

Order **Clathrinida**: probably 1 British species.

Clathrina coriacea forms a compact low-lying anastomosing mesh-like mass of simple delicate tubes. Typically white in colour. Oscula are not distinct. Choanocytes line the walls of the aquiferous canals. The larvae are flagellate over their whole surface.

Order **Leucettida**: probably 1 British species, *Leucaltis impressa.*

Choanocytes are confined to chambers off the aquiferous canals. The larvae are flagellate over their whole surface.

Subclass Calcaronea

The triactine spicules have rays of unequal length, set at unequal angles.

Order **Leucosoleniida**: probably 3 British species in a single family.

The sponge body is composed of delicate tubes, some simple and some branched, those bearing oscula at their tip grow away from the substratum. Choanocytes line the walls of the aquiferous canals. The spicules are triactines, with unequal basal angles, and one ray longer than the others. Typically white in colour. The larvae are flagellate only over their anterior hemisphere.

Order **Sycettida**: probably 7 British species in 4 families.

An Order of more regularly-shaped sponges, including the cylindrical *Scypha ciliata* (or *Sycon ciliata*) and the collapsed-purse *Grantia compressa* (or *Scypha compressa*). Some triactine spicules have unequal basal angles, and one ray longer than the others. Choanocytes are confined to chambers off the aquiferous canals. The larvae are flagellate only over their anterior hemisphere.

Class Demospongiae

Mostly marine sponges with a skeleton of spongin fibres sometimes reinforced with siliceous spicules. In many species, the spicules are divisible into megascleres (mostly monactines or tetractines) and microscleres (of diverse types). In some cases, the skeleton is supplemented with, dominated by, or entirely composed of, spongin. A very few species lack a skeleton altogether. Classification is based on reproductive patterns, larval morphology, spicule and other skeletal characters. More than 90% of living sponges belong to this Class. See Ackers, Moss, Picton & Stone (1985).

Subclass Homoscleromorpha

Sponges without a skeleton, of with a simple set of small (<100µm) spicules, including triactines, that are not differentiated into megascleres and microscleres.

Order **Homosclerophorida**: perhaps 4 British species.

The sponge lacks any skeletal material, is soft and fragile. *Oscarella lobularis* forms a 'bubbly' sheet over boulders or rock faces, perhaps extending 30cm.

Subclass Tetractinomorpha

Sponges with large spicules, radial or axial skeletons and often of a massive growth form. The megascleres (when present) are diactines or tetractines: microscleres are typically star shaped.

Order **Astrophorida** = **Choristida**: perhaps 19 British species in 5 families.

Sponges which may produce massive, rounded or plate-like forms. Megascleres always present, microscleres typically so. Eggs are extruded from the body and develop externally.

Order **Spirophorida**: perhaps 3 British species in 1 family.

The radial skeleton produces a spherical growth form. Oscula single, or in a small group, or not visible. Megascleres triactines and diactines. Microscleres of a characteristic contorted sigmoid form called sigmaspira. Eggs are either retained within the body or are extruded to develop externally. Typically, they live in soft substrata anchored by a basal mat of tangled spicules.

Order **Hadromerida**: perhaps 53 British species in 9 families.

The megascleres are pin-shaped monactines (tylostyles or subtylostyles) whilst any microscleres are asters. Spongin is typically present but not arranged in fibres. Many species form massive globular structures, with the oscula grouped into a common exit (or exits). *Cliona* sp. burrow into calcareous substrata.

Order **Axinellida**: perhaps 48 British species in 7 families.

Erect, funnel, tree or bush-shaped sponges, whose bodies incorporate appreciable amounts of spongin fibres – rendering the periphery flexible around a more rigid axial skeleton, which often lacks microscleres.

Subclass Ceractinomorpha

Viviparous sponges in which the megascleres are all monaxons. The microscleres are typically chelate and stigmate; never asterose.

Order **Halichondrida**: perhaps 10 British species in 2 families.

Mostly encrusting or cushion-forming sponges, whose skeleton lacks microscleres. The megascleres appear disordered, apparently lacking structure, except at the surface where they may be seen to be arranged tangentially. The parenchymella larvae are ciliated over their whole surface, and incubated within the body.

Order **Poecilosclerida**: perhaps 130 British species in 14 families.

Skeleton composed of both spicules and spongin fibres. Mostly encrusting forms. Megascleres show a range of monactine and diactine forms: microscleres very variable. The parenchymella larvae lack cilia over their posterior pole, and are incubated within the body.

Order **Haplosclerida**: possibly as many as 30 British marine species.
Taxonomy confused at family, genus and species level – the *Haliclona*s. Generally tubular, bush or tree-like sponges. The small, stout, diactine megascleres are arranged in an isodyctial skeleton, consolidated with spongin. Microscleres absent. The parenchymella larvae are not ciliated over their whole surface, and are incubated. This is the Order that includes freshwater sponges.

Order **Nepheliospongida**: 1 British species.

Order **Dictyoceratida**: perhaps 3 British species.
Sponges without spicules, the skeleton being formed of a mass of anatomising spongin fibres. The large parenchymella larvae have very long posterior cilia, and are incubated within the body. This Order includes the commercially-exploited (non-British) genus, *Spongia*.

Order **Dendroceratida**: perhaps 3 British species.
Sponges without spicules, the skeleton of spongin fibres is absent (Halisarcidae) or arranged in a dendritic pattern (Aplysillidae). The large parenchymella larvae are not ciliated over their whole surface, and are incubated.

Order **Verongida**: 1 British species.
Sponges without spicules, the reduced spongin skeleton supports a heavily collagenous matrix. Eggs extruded.

Phylum CNIDARIA

Cnidarians, better known under their former name of coelenterates (which included the Ctenophora as well), comprise jellyfish, sea anemones and corals. They fundamentally have radial symmetry and their bodies are essentially tubes, closed at one end and open at the other. The walls of the tube are composed of three layers – an outer epidermis, an inner gastrodermis, and a gelatinous mesoglea in-between. At the margins of the tube's open end, there are tentacles which bear thread or sting cells (cnidocytes, containing the nematocysts) to catch their prey – all are carnivores – and deter attackers.

The basic cnidarian life-cycle involves a succession of stages (sometimes, mistakenly, called an alternation of generations) between an asexual (often juvenile) polyp and a sexual (adult) medusa. In most cnidarians, the polyp is sedentary and benthic whereas the medusa is free-swimming and planktonic. Medusae bear gonads and the zygote develops, via a planula larva, into a polyp. There is, however, considerable variation in this pattern tending towards a simplification. To the layman, the different groups within the Cnidaria appear to be characterised by the degree of prominence shown by polyp and medusoid stages.

Taxonomic revision is proceeding at different rates in the separate major groups. Other works operate at least one grade lower. Hayward & Ryland (1995), for example, rank the Hydrozoa as a Class.

Sub-Phylum MEDUSOZOA

Cnidarians in which the medusa is usually an important stage in the life cycle, although, in some forms, it may be reduced to a bud on the polyp.

Super-Class Hydrozoa

Both polyp and medusa phases occur, although either may be reduced or be absent. The gelatinous mesoglea is partly acellular. Cnidocytes are confined to the epidermis. Polyps (hydroids) are radially symmetrical with a cylindrical coelenteron that is not partitioned by radial septa. It is, however, often protected by a chitinous cup (hydrotheca). The well-known freshwater *Hydra* is a genus of solitary species, but most others are colonial with the individual polyps connected by tubes (coenosarc). Individual polyps may be specialised for different functions. Typical medusae are small transparent planktonic animals, which have the mouth hanging on a hollow stalk from the centre of the lower (adumbral) surface of the bell. A thin shelf of tissue, called the velum, extends inwards from the margin of the bell.

The early workers did not recognise hydroids and medusae as different stages in one life cycle, and two independent classifications arose. It has taken many years of research to link sufficient of the named hydroids to named medusae for a coherent taxonomy to be accepted (see Cornelius, 1995a). Inevitably, this has involved the introduction of new names, for the old ones referred either to hydroids or to medusae.

Class Leptolida

Hydroids, hydromedusae, 'the hydras' and similar forms.

Five of the seven Subclasses are represented in British waters. The basic leptolid life cycle comprises both hydroid and medusa stages but, in some groups, either one or the other is suppressed to some degree, and may be essentially bypassed. There is structural variation in both stages, where they exist, between groups.

Subclass Limnomedusae

Order **Limnomedusa**: 4 British marine species, in 2 families.

A mainly-freshwater Order in which the polyps are typically solitary (the family Proboscidactylidae is an exception) and have few (or no) tentacles. The hydrotheca is thin or absent. Hydroid colonies of the marine species *Proboscidactyla stellata* (formerly known as *Lar sabellarum*) are minute, stolonal, rarely recorded and then only from around the aperture of sabellid worm tubes (Medusae have been recorded all around Britain). A series of single, naked, gastrozooids (of 'quasi-humanoid' form) grow on from an anastomosing stolon. Less than 1mm high, they have just two long tentacles. Medusae have hollow tentacles; statocysts are internal. See Russell (1953).

Subclass Narcomedusae

Order **Narcomedusa**: 7 British species in 3 families.

Development is direct in these oceanic medusae, without an intervening polyp stage, although some (non-British) species have planula larvae parasitic on other cnidarians. Typically the bell is flatter than hemispherical, with a central lens-shaped mass of jelly and much thinner sides. Margin lobed, segmented into wide flaps by deep radial divisions. The tentacles are solid and inserted on the exumbral surface, well in from the margin. There are no radial canals. The circular canal is absent or looped into the marginal flaps to form a peripheral canal. Manubrium typically short; statocysts ecto- endodermal. The gonads, encircling the manubrium, are large and simple in shape or have marginal pockets intruding into the stomach. See Bouillon, (1987) or Russell (1953).

Subclass Trachymedusae

Order **Trachymedusa**: 7 British species in 3 families.

Development is direct in these small oceanic hydromedusae, without an intervening polyp stage. They are seldom coastal, being mainly restricted to deeper water. The bell is tall to hemispherical. Margin entire with a peripheral ring of nematocysts. Radial canals and circular canals are present. Gonads only on the radial canals. Tentacles are either all solid, or a mixture of solid and hollow. Statocysts ecto-endodermal, open or closed. See Bouillon, (1987) or Russell (1953).

Subclass Actinulidae

Order **Actinula**: about 4 British species.

Minute interstitial forms, said superficially to recall the freshwater *Hydra* in shape, but this may be simply as a result of their minute size and general simplicity. Typically about 1mm long. Few species are known but individuals can be locally common in clean sandy shores of large grain size, especially in regions of intertidal run-off. Two genera are currently admitted. For literature see Werner (1984a) and Bouillon (1985a).

The body structure recalls that of an actinula larva, rather than a typical leptolid medusa or hydroid stage, as the mouth opens at the opposite end of the body from the tentacles! Solitary, tiny, ciliated (flagellated) externally. The open ecto-endodermal statocysts are similar to those of narcomedusans. Development direct.

Subclass Anthoathecatae: about 60 British marine species (two extending almost into fresh water) in 2 Orders (Filifera and Capitata) and some 14 families.

Medusae (anthomedusae) are released in many genera, but suppressed or retained on the colony in others. The much reduced freshwater *Hydra* and its related forms are now included here. When present, the medusa is, typically, bell-shaped. Gonads are found only on the manubrium or, in a few species, on the most basal regions of the radial canals. Sense organs, if present, are ocelli (light-receptors), never statocysts or cordyli (tiny club-shaped structures hanging from the bell margin). Tentacles peripheral.

The hydroids may be either solitary or colonial. Hydrotheca, nematotheca and gonotheca are absent (but a frail, membranous secondarily-evolved pseudohydrotheca is present in a few species – e.g., some *Eudendrium* in W Europe). The branches and stolons of a colony are, typically, protected by a strong chitinous 'perisarc', in some species with calcareous elements. However, the perisarc is reduced in several common genera which have a mat-like hydrorhiza lacking discrete strands (e.g. *Hydractinia* and the neustonic *Velella*, in which it forms a float.). See Russell (1953, 1970) for British species and, for a recent review of the world's genera, see Bouillon (1985a).

Velella velella (the by-the-wind sailor) was once referred to an Order of its own (Chondrophora) but is now relegated to a family (Velellidae). This highly distinctive animal floats on the ocean surface, but is sporadically stranded (sometimes in large numbers) on western coasts. After death, the thin transparent skeleton appears like a discarded piece of plastic on the strandline but, in life, the deep blue raft-like float, up to 10cm in length (but often only half that size), bears a triangular fin set diagonally across its upper surface that acts as a sail. Tentacles, bearing stinging cells, hang from the float. Medusae, bearing two tentacles on release, with bunches of nematocysts at the ends, are released from gonozooids hanging below the float. See Kirkpatrick & Pugh (1984).

Subclass Leptothecatae

The medusa (leptomedusa) is, typically, flatter than hemispherical; many are saucer-shaped. Gonads are borne on the radial canals, exceptionally on the manubrium. Sense organs, if present, are ectodermal statocysts or cordyli, rarely ocelli. The many tentacles are peripheral.

Most of the hydroids are typically found with specialised polyp-cups, variously termed hydrothecae, nematothecae and gonothecae according to the specialised function of the polyp it protects. In most species, the hydrotheca is large enough for the hydranth (feeding polyp) to fit inside. Alas, in some groups (e.g. Haleciidae) it is short (like a priest's collar) and, since they also have large hydranths, this can cause confusion with anthoathecates (see opposite). The gonophore is protected within a gonotheca, or in a more elaborate structure. See Cornelius (1995); Russell (1953: 1970).

Order **Conica**

Leptothecatae in which the hydranth has a conical hypostome. The group is based on hydroid characters (regardless of the medusa) and includes all but one of the leptothecate families in the area. It is a somewhat unsatisfactory grouping and one or more of the following Suborders may be promoted to ordinal rank.

Suborder Campanulinida: 34 British species in 13 families.

A group of tiny hydroids, most of which liberate typical hydromedusae. The hydranths of most are fully retractable into hydrothecae and further protected by a conical operculum, or by one with the form of a gabled roof. Although these tiny hydroids can have little environmental impact, their medusae (which in *Staurophora mertensii* can reach 300mm diameter) are important prey of many plankton carnivores, including some commercial fish.

Suborder Lafoeida: 4 British species in a single family.

None of our four species releases a medusa (although, elsewhere, other members of the group do so). The hydrotheca lacks an operculum. Both hydranth and hydrotheca are radially symmetrical in almost all species.

Suborder Haleciida: 12 British species in a single family.

Several of our species form large and conspicuous colonies in coastal waters. The hydranth is much too large for its hydrotheca which lacks an operculum in some species. Both the hydranth and the hydrotheca are radially symmetrical. Most species do not release medusae.

Suborder Plumulariida: 51 British species in 4 families.

Most hydroids that form large colonies are included in this Suborder. The hydrotheca lacks an operculum. The hydranth and its hydrotheca, into which it can retract, often show some secondary bilateral symmetry. The medusa is typically suppressed but a few species release a vestigial one.

Order **Proboscoidea**

Leptothecatae in which the hydranth has a flared to globose hypostome, effectively forming a buccal cavity beneath the mouth.

Suborder Campanulariida: 19 British species in a single family.

The only UK family, Campanulariidae, has hydranths with stalked, bell-shaped hydrothecae that lack opercula. The also lack nematophores. Medusae are released by only a minority of species.

Class Siphonophora: 55 species have been recorded from British waters.

Siphonophores are highly polymorphic, colonial, planktonic often bilaterally-symmetrical marine hydroids. None is truly British, in that it lives permanently in our waters: their occurrence depends on the occasional intrusion of oceanic water onto our continental shelf or, in the case of *Physalia physalis*, the Portuguese man o' war, prevailing winds driving them into shallow water. This, the best known species, is a floating colony from which the medusae are not released. The individual polyps (zooids), which display a high level of polymorphism, are clustered beneath a large float (pneumatophore). See Kirkpatrick & Pugh (1984).

Super-Class Scyphozoa

In jellyfish, the medusa is the dominant phase; typically large and free-swimming, with gastrodermal gonads, cellular mesoglea but lacking a velum. Symmetry is typically tetramerous. The polyp is small (but long-lived), with the coelenteron partitioned by 4 septa. All species are marine.

Order **Stauromedusae**: 7 British species in 2 families.

Stalked jellyfish are medusae attached, aborally, to algae or hard substrates. The mouth faces upwards. All but one of the British species have 8 'arms' bearing small tentacles and, typically, have adhesive anchors on the webs between the arms. Sexes are separate. They are probably annuals. See Hayward & Ryland (1990; 1995).

Order **Coronatae**: 7 British species in 4 families.

Deep-water, and deeply-coloured, jellyfish in which the bell is divided into upper and lower regions by a groove. The bell margin is deeply scalloped. The tentacles, which alternate with sense organs around the margin of the bell, are solid. See Russell (1970).

Order **Semaeostomae**: 5 British species in 3 families.

Coastal jellyfish in which the bell is entire, typically with an even, or shallowly-lobed, margin. The corners of the mouth are drawn-out into four frilly lobes. The hollow marginal tentacles are evenly-arranged around the bell or clumped. See Russell (1970).

Order **Rhizostomae**: 1 British species.

Rhizostoma octopus is a coastal jellyfish in which the bell is entire but is without marginal tentacles. The mouth region has 4 long lobes which divide into 8 thick arms and develop into a sponge-like filter-feeding organ with many thousands of mouths. Many small openings in these arms form secondary, suctorial, mouths. See Russell (1970).

Sub-Phylum ANTHOZOA

Cnidarians without a medusoid stage in the life cycle. The polyp is large (sometimes very large) with a thick cellular mesoglea and with the coelenteron partitioned by mesenteries. Individuals are either solitary or colonial. See Manuel (1980) and (1988).

Class Octocorallia

Colonial. The individual polyps are typically small. All have 8 pinnate tentacles and 8 perfect mesenteries.

Order **Stolonifera**: 2 British species in separate families.
Polyps arise singly from a narrow creeping stolon, without secondary budding. Colonies form encrusting networks by branching and anastomosing, occasionally forming membranous sheets.

Order **Alcyonacea**: 3 British species in a single family.
Soft corals or dead man's fingers. The colonies form encrusting sheets or erect fleshy masses.

Order **Gorgonacea**: 2 British species in separate families.
Sea fans form attached, branching, tree-like colonies. In the two British species, reaching between 150 and 300mm high.

Order **Pennatulacea**: 4 British species in 3 families.
Sea pens form unattached colonies, living upright with their stalks thrust into mud or sand. See Williams (1995) for an overview and key to species.

Class Hexacorallia

Colonial or solitary. The individual polyps may be large or small but never have just 8 pinnate tentacles and 8 perfect mesenteries; tentacles and mesenteries are typically numerous.

Order **Ceriantharia**: at least 3 British species in 2 families.
The solitary polyps live in tubes buried in soft substrata. Unlike all other Anthozoa, they have two series of tentacles: a labial series arising from around the mouth and a marginal series arising from the periphery of the disc. The column is rounded at the aboral end, elongated and very contractile. Arachnactis larvae, which float passively at the surface of the sea, are collected more easily than adults and their variety suggests that further species await description. See Leloup (1962) for Arachnactis larvae

Order **Zoantharia**: 8 British species in 2 families.
All British species are colonial. The colonies comprise numerous polyps arising from within an encrusting coenchymatous mass, typically encrusted, in turn, with sand or other particulate matter. Some species live (commensally?) on gastropod shells occupied by hermit crabs. In mature 'carcinoecia', the shell is dissolved away and crab lives directly within the zoanthid colony.

Order **Actiniaria**: 45 British species in 13 families.
True sea anemones are solitary polyps which never possess a calcareous skeleton. The tentacles, which are never knobbed at the ends, may form several whorls but they all arise from the margin of the disc. The base typically forms an adhesive disc, but it may be rounded in burrowing forms.

Order **Corallimorpharia**: 1 British species.
The jewel anemone, *Corynactis viridis*, is easily distinguished from other anemone-like polyps by its knobbed tentacles. Asexual reproduction, by longitudinal fission, is often imperfect so that daughter anemones remain connected to their parent by strands of basal tissue.

Order **Scleractinia**: 6 British species in 2 families.

Stone corals may be solitary or colonial, but all have an external calcareous skeleton secreted by the base and walls of the polyp. The structure of the polyp is similar to those of the Corallimorpharia, including knobbed tentacles. The tentacles are retractile (in British species) and studded with tiny wart-like nematocyst batteries.

Phylum CTENOPHORA

Sea gooseberries and comb-jellies are predatory, mostly pelagic, marine animals. Their basic organisation is comparable with that of a cnidarian medusa but is triploblastic. Like cnidarians, the nervous system forms a loose network but (unlike cnidarians) the gut has anal pores as well as a mouth. The animals swim by the beating of their unique comb plates (blocks of fused cilia) which are arranged in eight longitudinal comb-rows, running the length of the body. Beating is co-ordinated via an apical ganglion, and the animal moves mouth first in search of its prey. Victims are caught by lasso cells (the ctenophore functional equivalent of cnidocytes) on the very long, retractile, tentacles. Most ctenophores are simultaneous hermaphrodites with external fertilisation. Larvae are planktonic. See Greve (1975).

Class Tentaculata

Sea gooseberries; with two tentacles.

Order **Cydippida**: 1 British species.

Pleurobrachia pileus is one of the most abundant members of the British coastal plankton, with a nearly spherical body, well developed comb rows and tentacle sheaths. (All tentaculate ctenophores pass through a larval stage with cydippid features: some of the described species may, actually, be the larvae of adults in other Orders).

Order **Lobata**: 1 British species.

Bolinopsis infundibulum has a pear-shaped body with large oral lobes in the adult. Tentacles are short and located close to the mouth.

Class Nuda

Comb-jellies without tentacles at any stage in the life cycle. These predators of other ctenophores have a wide and flexible mouth, and a body largely occupied by the capacious 'stomach'.

Order **Beroida**: 2 British species in a single family.

Both species of *Beroe* look somewhat like airships. *B. gracilis*, which reaches 30mm in length, preys exclusively on *Pleurobrachia*: given the choice, *B. cucumis* prefers *Bolinopsis*.

Phylum PLATYHELMINTHES

Platyhelminths (flatworms, flukes and tapeworms) are bilaterally-symmetrical, pseudocoelomate, unsomited, worm-like animals with soft, dorso-ventrally flattened bodies. The animals have organ systems but no body cavity. The gut is blind-ended with the combined mouth and anus on the ventral side. There are no circulatory or respiratory systems. Free-living species all have a distinct head, bearing simple sense organs. All platyhelminths feed on animal tissues, whether as carnivores, scavengers or parasites. All are capable of extensive regeneration of lost tissues: some breed more by asexual than sexual means.

Of the five Classes currently recognised, the Aspidogastraea, Digenea, Monogenea and Cestoda are entirely parasitic – on a wide range of hosts which includes crustacea, molluscs and vertebrates. For a general account of the parasitic forms, see Pearse *et al.* (1987). Most Turbellaria are free-living, and most are marine, although there are terrestrial and freshwater representatives in Britain.

Class Turbellaria

Almost all are free-living flatworms with an eversible pharynx and, typically, a lobed (branched) intestine. The cellular and ciliated epidermis contains rhabdites (rod-like structures of uncertain function). Movement is effected by cilia on the ventral surface (gliding) and/or by muscular contractions. Many are small simple animals, interstitial in habit. Hartog (1974) illustrates the difficulty in defining marine species. He lists 56 species on North-western European saltmarshes split between marine, littoral, salt-marsh, brackish water and euryhaline forms.

Order **Acoela**: at least 13 British species in 4 families.

Small, often interstitial, marine flatworms without a permanent gut cavity, or protonephridia. For many years, they were considered to be syncitial until electron microscopy revealed cell membranes. They are without yolk glands, oviducts or membranes around the gonads. A statocyst is present. Species of *Avagina*; are found in burrowing sea urchins: *Convoluta* and the others are free-living on the shore, especially among algae and sea grasses.

Order **Catenulida**: 1 British species.

A small group of delicate, elongate, interstitial (650µm), mainly freshwater flatworms with a simple pharynx and a sac-like gut, but without an oviduct or yolk glands. Members of the marine family, Retronectidae, live in sands under sheltered conditions. *Retronectes terpsichore* (Sterrer & Rieger, 1974) lives intertidally in detritus-rich coarse sand, near to the black layer.

Order **Macrostomatida**: at least 5 British species in 1 family.

Marine or freshwater flatworms with a simple pharynx, a sac-like gut, paired excretory ducts and a complete reproductive system, which none-the-less lacks yolk glands. No statocyst.

Order **Neorhabdocoela**: at least 33 British species in 10 families.

Marine, freshwater and terrestrial flatworms with a complex bulbous pharynx, straight, non-ciliated gut, separate ovaries and yolk glands. Some species are commensal or parasitic: members of the family Umagillidae are associated with echinoderms; those in the family Graffillidae with molluscs. Free-living species are found amongst sea grasses and intertidal algae.

Order **Seriata**: at least 6 British species in 1 family.

Interstitial, mostly marine, flatworms with a tubular pharynx hanging in a large pharyngeal cavity. The gut is unbranched. Yolk glands are present and there is a distinctive statocyst. They often have adhesive structures at their posterior end.

Order **Tricladida**

Suborder Maricola: perhaps 6 British marine species in 2 families.

Probably the best-known Order of Turbellarians, planarians are an ubiquitous group of wide occurrence on land, in the sea and in fresh waters. The tubular folded pharynx retracts into a large cavity. The intestine is divided into a single anterior and 2 posterior diverticulated branches (only visible in pale individuals). Marine representatives grow up to 7mm long and have two eyes. Only two are common in Britain – *Procerodes ulvae* (which lives where freshwater streams run over the shore) and *Uteriporus vulgaris* (which may be common on salt marshes). All British species are carnivores/scavengers except *Micropharynx parasitica* which is an ectosymbiont/ectoparasite of skates. See Ball & Reynoldson (1981) and Sluys (1989) for *Micropharynx*.

Order **Polycladida**: 19 British marine species in 9 families.

Comparatively large (one British species may reach 40mm), and sometimes brightly-coloured, these are greatly flattened active flatworms. Many have the ability to float or to glide on the underside of the surface film. British polyclads are all marine in habit. The folded pharynx leads to an intestine with numerous lateral branches (visible in pale specimens). Some have cephalic tentacles, none has a statocyst. Compared with freshwater triclads, all have poor powers of regeneration. Some species have a ciliated, planktonic, 'Müller's larva' in their life cycle.

A few species are common between the tide marks, but most are found from between low water mark and 40m. See Prudhoe (1982) and (1985).

Class Monogenea: at least 60 British species.

Flat, leaf-shaped flukes, mostly ectoparasitic on the gills, fins and skin of fish, although *Undonilla caligorus* is a hyperparasite of *Caligus* (copepod) on *Labrus bergylta* (fish). The eggs hatch into an onchomiracidia larva which attaches to the host, and then changes gradually into the adult form. The body is covered by a well-developed cuticle and has (often multiple) organs of attachment – suckers, hooks and clamps – at both ends. The larval stage does not multiply asexually. Llewellyn *et al.*, (1984) list 60 species of Monogeneans from marine fish and cephalopods off Plymouth.

Order **Monopisthocotylea**

Body with a single posterior and paired anterior attachment organs. Without a genito-intestinal canal.

Order **Polyopisthocotylea**

Body with two or more posterior attachment organs, and with either a single oral sucker or a pair of buccal suckers anteriorly. With a genito-intestinal canal.

Class Aspidogastrea

A small group of flukes, often regarded as midway between the Monogenea and Digenea (and, with them, at one time, considered a Subclass of the Trematoda). Adults are typically endoparasitic in freshwater or marine molluscs, but also occur in fish and turtles. The fluke has a cylindrical, often worm-like, body with a ventral haptor (holdfast). The mouth is surrounded by a buccal funnel but the rest of the body lacks hooks and anchors. Development is typically direct but some species have an intermediate host.

Class Digenea: at least 51 British marine species in 14 families.

Endoparasitic flukes, mostly in vertebrates when adult, but with a complicated life cycle that involves one or more intermediate hosts. The first intermediate host is typically a mollusc. In British coastal species, the second is often a fish or crustacean that is subsequently eaten by a larger fish or by a bird. There are several larval stages, one or more of which multiplies asexually.

Class Cestoda: at least 25 British marine species in 6 families.

Tapeworms are mostly intestinal parasites of vertebrates, when adult. The body is without a mouth or gut and is attached to the intestinal wall of its host by the scolex, which bears hooks and/or suckers. Behind the scolex, the strobila – a linear series of proglottids – is formed. Each develops a set of reproductive organs and matures as it is distanced from the scolex by younger proglottids. Eventually it fills with eggs. These develop into onchosphere larvae, with six hooks, which leave the vertebrate and infect an intermediate host.

Phylum GNATHOSTOMULIDA

Gnathostomulids resemble turbellarian flatworms in being ciliated and elongate semitransparent hermaphroditic worms (0.2-3mm long) without an anus and without a body cavity. Indeed, they were initially included in the Turbellaria, but as their distinctive features were appreciated, they were removed first to a separate new class of flatworms and then to this new phylum. Their phylogenetic relationships remain uncertain. Fewer than 100 species have been described but many more are known, and the rate a which new ones are discovered in new locations suggests a eventual total close to 1,000.

They live intertidally in the black anaerobic layer of fine-grained sandy beaches, where the smell of hydrogen sulphide suggests that nothing can live. The feeding apparatus, found in most species, consists of a little pair of hard, toothed jaws and a central basal plate. With these, gnathostomulids scrape Cyanobacteria ('blue-green algae'), diatoms, fungal filaments, bacteria, and other organic matter from the surfaces of sand grains.

The epidermis is one cell-layer thick and is monociliated, each epidermal cell bearing a single long cilium. Sensory structures on the head may include a halo of stiff sensory cilia, single or compound, and ciliary pits. Gnathostomulids are further distinguished from flatworms by their scant mesenchyme and striated muscles, by a different type of protonephridia (with single flagella instead of with tufts of many flagella), and by their sperm structure. When flagellated, gnathostomulid sperms have only a single flagellum with the usual 9 + 2 arrangement of microtubules. The flagella of flatworm sperms almost always occur in pairs and have different microtubular patterns.

Although occasionally found on algal fronds or sea grasses, gnathostomulids are predominantly interstitial, living in the spaces between sand grains in or near the organically-rich anaerobic black layer. Respiration is (mainly ?) anaerobic: they have not been kept alive in aquaria, perhaps partly because they are exposed to too much oxygen

Gnathostomulids show many of the typical characters of interstitial animals: small size, elongate shape, absence of eyes and the ability to cling to the surface of sand grains. Finding a mate presents special problems in this habitat, but these are gregarious and hermaphroditic animals so that any encounter with another sexually mature individual of the same species can result in copulation. Such tiny animals can produce only a few gametes. Gnathostomulids lay single yolky eggs which develop directly into the adult form, without any swimming larval stage. See Pearse *et al.* (1987)

Phylum MESOZOA

A small group of enigmatic, ciliated, bilaterally-symmetrical endoparasites, composed of a small number of cells and without any muscular, nervous, digestive, respiratory, excretory or skeletal systems. The vermiform body comprises an outer layer of somatic cells enclosing one or more large axial germinative cells. Life histories are complex and involve an alternation of sexual and asexual generations. Regarded as degenerate platyhelminths or a multicellular group separately evolved from protoctistans. See Barnes (1984)

Class Rhombozoa
Both the sexual and asexual phases are kidney parasites of cephalopod molluscs. The short-lived infusoriform larva is the only free-living stage in the life cycle.
Class Orthonectida
The sexual phase is free-living: the asexual phase is a tissue parasite of a marine invertebrate. The free-living animals are worm-like.

Phylum NEMERTEA

Ribbon worms are elongate, bilaterally-symmetrical, unsomited, worm-like animals with soft bodies that are often capable of extreme contraction and elongation. In size, British species range from a few millimetres in length (*Carcinonemertes*) to more than 30 metres (*Lineus*) although most are less than 30cm. There is no true head. In most species, the front end is rounded or blunted although some genera do have a cephalic lobe (not a head because it does not, normally, house the cerebral ganglion). The cephalic region may bear distinct furrows (cephalic grooves). The number of eyes, in those species which retain them in the adult, ranges from 2 to many. In those species with between two and six eyes, the number is typically constant. The mouth is subterminal and, during feeding, can be enormously distended to ingest large prey items. At the other extremity of the body, the anus opens at, or just above, the posterior end – which may taper gently to a sharp or blunt tip, but sometimes bears a caudal cirrus.

Members of the bathypelagic Order Polystilifera (which, as they generally live at depths greater than 500m, can hardly be considered British) float passively or swim in a slow and sluggish manner, but most adult nemerteans move freely over hard surfaces, burrow in sediments or squeeze themselves into crevices – typically by waves of muscle contraction passing in either direction along the body. During locomotion, the shape and diameter of the body alters very considerably.

Many species are oviparous and, in most, the sexes are separate, although some are hermaphrodite and at least one species is ovoviviparous, giving birth to live young. More typically, gametes are shed into sea water and fertilisation is external without the parents coming into direct contact. Three types of larvae are recognised – the Desor larva grows entirely within the egg membrane whereas the pilidium (somewhat resembling an annelid trochophore) Iwata larvae escape from their egg cases and are pelagic for a while. Pilidium larvae feed but the others do not. The life cycle is probably a year, although some have been kept for longer in aquaria.

Most nemerteans are free-living hunting carnivores (of turbellarians, nematodes, annelids, crustaceans, molluscs or fishes) or scavengers. *Malacobdella grossa*, however, lives inside the shells of bivalve molluscs and filter feeds within the host's mantle chamber. *Carcinonemertes carcinophila* lives on the gills and egg masses of crabs and squat lobsters.

Of the 80 British species, one (an immigrant) is terrestrial in habit, two are found in freshwater and all the rest are marine (see Gibson, 1995).

Class Anopla

The mouth lies below, or posterior to, the cerebral ganglia. The central nervous system runs within the body wall. The proboscis is of uniform construction along its length and is either unarmed, or is provided with large numbers of rhabdite-like epithelial barbs.

Order: **Archinemertea**: 3 British species in a single family.

Body wall musculature is primarily composed of two layers of musculature (outer circular and inner longitudinal). Some taxa have an incomplete inner circular muscle layer, restricted to the foregut region. The dermis is composed of hyaline connective tissue. The central nervous system is situated entirely in the (body wall) longitudinal muscle layer.

Order **Palaeonemertea**: 12 British species in 2 families.

Body wall is composed either of two (outer circular and inner longitudinal) or of three (outer circular, middle longitudinal and inner circular) layers of musculature. The dermis is composed of hyaline connective tissue. The central nervous system typically runs in the inner longitudinal musculature but, in some taxa, extends into the longitudinal muscle layer (but only in the intestinal region)

Order **Heteronemertea**: 26 British species in 3 families.

The body wall is composed of three layers of musculature (outer longitudinal, middle circular and inner longitudinal). The dermis is well developed and, normally, is composed of fibrous connective tissue and gland cells. The central nervous system runs between the outer longitudinal and middle circular layers of circular musculature.

Class Enopla

The mouth lies in front of the cerebral ganglia. The central nervous system runs internal to the body wall musculature – which is two layered (outer circular and inner longitudinal). The proboscis is typically differentiated into three regions and, typically, is armed with two or more needle-like stylets.

Order Hoplonemertea

Proboscis armed with one or more stylets; intestine straight, mostly with paired lateral diverticula; no posterior ventral sucker.

Suborder Monostilifera: 33 British marine species in 7 families.

The proboscis is armed with a single central stylet carried on a large cylindrical basis. The intestine is straight, with paired lateral diverticula. The animal is without a posterior sucker. Most species are free-living but *Tetrastemma fozensis* lives in the mantle cavity of the bivalve *Scrobicularia plana*.

Suborder Polystilifera Tribe Reptantia: 2 British marine species in 2 families.

Free-living crawling or burrowing forms. The proboscis armature forms a pad, or shield, bearing numerous small stylets. The intestine is straight, with paired lateral diverticula.

Order Bdellonemertea: 1 British species.

Malacobdella grossa is an entocommensal in bivalve molluscs. The proboscis is unarmed. The intestine is sinuous and without paired lateral diverticula. The animal has a posterior sucker. *M. grossa* reaches 40mm in length; young are white but the adult female is greenish grey and the male pinkish. It has been reported from 23 bivalve mollusc host species, but is particularly common in the gaper, *Mya truncata* and the piddock *Zirfaea crispata*.

Phylum GASTROTRICHA

Hair animalcules are small (< 4mm long), free-living, unsomited, bilaterally-symmetrical, worm-like aquatic animals living interstitially in beach sand. Their oval to elongate, dorsoventrally-flattened bodies end in a thin 'tail', in a fork, or in a rounded shape. Like turbellarian platyhelminths, they are without respiratory or circulatory systems. The dorsal surface bears a monociliar covering and cilia are also present ventrally, in various patterns, being used in the creeping form of locomotion. Dorsally and laterally, the body may bear scales, spines, hooks, and tubes which secrete adhesive material for temporary attachment to the substratum. The gut has both mouth and anus and a muscular pharynx. The nervous system comprises a large cerebral ganglion, longitudinal cords, and various anterior sense organs. Most species are hermaphroditic, although some show parthenogenesis. Boaden (1963) provides a key to the 28 species found in intertidal sand on Anglesey and around the Lleyn Peninsula, N. Wales.

Order Macrodasyida: at least 8 British marine species in 3 families.

Marine. With pharyngeal pores. The strap-like body bears anterior, lateral and at least 6 pairs of posterior adhesive tubules. Hermaphroditic.

Order Chaetonotida: at least 20 British marine species in 5 families.

Freshwater and marine. Without pharyngeal pores. The fusiform body bears two adhesive tubules posteriorly, which form the posterior feet. Hermaphroditic or parthenogenetic.

Phylum ROTIFERA

Wheel animalcules are small (< 2mm long), mostly free-living, unsomited, bilaterally-symmetrical aquatic animals. They lead a swimming, crawling or sedentary existence, mostly in freshwater but also in the sea. The body is typically an elongated trumpet bearing, anteriorly, a characteristic wheel organ (corona) which is a crown of cilia used in locomotion and/or feeding. In all but the planktonic species, the other end of the body terminates in a foot, used for attachment to the substratum. The gut incorporates a mouth, anus and a muscular jaw-bearing pharynx. Sexes are separate, but males are not known for all species so parthenogenesis is suspected. There is no larval stage. (Note: live rotifers are very easily confused with tintinnid protoctistans.)

Class Seisonidea: perhaps a single British species.
> *Seison*; (the only genus in the Class) lives on the gills of the leptostracan crustacean *Nebalia*; and some isopods. Individuals are comparatively large (a few mm). Corona somewhat reduced. Both sexes are equally abundant.

Class Bdelloidea
> The worm-shaped body can be contracted by telescoping. Corona in the form of two wheels. The retractable foot bears up to four toes. Parthenogenetic.

Order **Bdelloida**: at least one British marine species.
> Most species are freshwater animals but *Zelinkiella synaptae* has been recorded on the tentacles and general body surface of holothurians.

Class Monogonata
> Most rotifers belong to this Class. The male, if known, is smaller than the female. The foot bears no more than two toes. See Berzins (1960).

Order **Ploima**: at least 30 British species, in 6 families, are estuarine or marine.
> A mostly planktonic Order in which the corona is in the form of a circumapical band. The foot, if present, has one or two toes and pedal glands.

Order **Flosculariida**: at least 4 British species, in 2 families, are estuarine or marine.
> An Order containing both sessile and planktonic rotifers, in which the circumapical coronal band is broken into two portions. The foot, if present, without toes but with numerous pedal glands.

Order **Collothecida**: 1 British estuarine species.
> An Order of sessile rotifers, inhabiting gelatinous tubes in which the circular, narrow, corona is without lobes. The long foot bears a terminal attachment disc. *Collotheca pelagica* is a freshwater species, also found in estuaries.

? Phylum ASCHELMINTHES?

Some authorities argue that the next five Phyla (Kinorhyncha, Priapula, Acanthocephala, Loricifera and Nematomorpha), should be regarded as Classes within the Aschelminthes; arguments that have been strengthened by the discovery of the Loricifera. In this case, I have adopted a traditional stance and listed them as separate Phyla.

Phylum KINORHYNCHA

Kinorhynchs are small (< 2mm long), stubby worm-shaped, free-living, bilaterally-symmetrical, aquatic animals. The body is divided externally into thirteen somites, but there is no comparable internal somitation. The body lacks cilia but is covered by a chitinous cuticle, divided into plates with flexible articulating regions in between. The first somite (head) and the second (neck) can be retracted into the body. The eleven trunk somites may bear long moveable, backwardly-directed spines. The gut is tubular with mouth, anus and a muscular pharynx. The nervous system comprises a multi-lobed brain, ventral longitudinal nerve cords with somitally-arranged ganglia. The sexes are separate and fertilisation is internal. See Higgins (1985) and McIntyre (1962).

 Order **Cyclorhagida**: 10 British marine species, in 3 families.
  When the head and neck are retracted into the trunk somites, plates on the neck close the opening. Mid-dorsal lateral spines and caudal spines are present. The trunk somites bear cuticular hairs or denticles.

 Order **Homalorhagida**: 6 British marine species in 2 families.
  When the head and neck are retracted into the trunk somites, plates on the third somite close the opening. There are no mid-dorsal or lateral spines and only one genus has caudal spines. The trunk somites are without cuticular hairs.

Phylum PRIAPULA

Penis worms are free-living bilaterally symmetrical benthic marine animals, with unsomited, but annulated, bodies, divided into two clearly-defined regions. The barrel-shaped proboscis, which can be withdrawn into the trunk by invagination, is alternately extruded and withdrawn to burrow. Prey is caught by curved teeth on the everted mouth and pharynx lining, drawn in and swallowed during withdrawal of the proboscis. The body is covered by an annulated chitinous cuticle, which is moulted periodically whilst, at the posterior end, there are bunches described by Barrett & Yonge (1958) as like 'ants-eggs'. Sexes are separate and fertilisation is typically external. The egg hatches into a loricate larva. There are 15 living species, world-wide.

Class Priapulida: 1, possibly 2, British species.
  Priapulus caudatus reaches 75mm in length and lives in grey (sometimes black) mud from the middle shore down into the sub-littoral. Locally common. An active carnivore, moving through the sediment. The mouth has 7 rings each of 5 teeth. See Stephen (1960).

Phylum ACANTHOCEPHALA

Adult spiny-headed worms are intestinal parasites of vertebrates, whilst the juveniles typically infest arthropods. They are bilaterally-symmetrical, cylindrical, unsomited (although often superficially annulated) animals, between 1mm and 1m in length. A proboscis armed with sclerotised hooks anchors the worm to the host's gut wall. They are without a mouth or gut but have a large pseudocoelomate cavity. Muscular, nervous and excretory systems are all reduced. There is no respiratory system. The sexes are separate, fertilisation is internal and there are three larval stages during the life cycle – acanthor, acanthella and cystacanth. *Profilicollis botulus* uses the crab *Carcinus maenas* as intermediate host en route towards infecting the eider duck *Somateria mollissima* as an adult. The Plymouth Marine Fauna (1957) records four species of Echinorhynchidae from fish intestines.

Phylum LORICIFERA

The Phylum was first described by Kristensen (1983). They are a group of very small interstitial animals (adults of the type species are only 235 μm long) which live interstitially in clean coarse marine sediments (sand or shelly gravel) and were discovered by chance when a marine sediment sample was washed with freshwater!

Loriciferans ('corset bearers') have a variety of aschelminth characters, and their discovery seems to make the Aschelminthes a more cohesive group. The vase-shaped lorica, in which most of the body is encased and for which the group is named, is constructed of 6 cuticular plates and looks much like that of some rotifers (and of larval priapulans). The mouth cone and spiny head, or introvert, which can be withdrawn and extended, resemble those of kinorhynchs. The mouth is surrounded by a circle of 8 or 9 stylets, and 2 accessory stylets appear to protrude into the digestive tract just in front of the muscular pharynx; these remind us of the stylets of larval nematomorphs (or of tardigrades). The simple digestive tract has one pair of glands and ends in slightly dorsal anus. The nervous system comprises a relative large dorsal brain, a circle of ganglia around the mouth, presumably associated with the spines, and two or more ventral ganglia. Sexes are separate. Growth and development are by moulting.

The Higgins larva (which is found in 2 discrete size classes) has only 4 main plates in the lorica, 3 pairs of ventral locomotory spines and a pair of leaflike posterior 'toes.' They climb slowly over sand grains using these ventral spines and the tips of their toes, or swim by paddling with the toes. Illustrations based on Kristensen (1983) make it look like an appealing if somewhat seedy character from a cartoon strip. See Pearce *et al.*, (1987).

The type specimen of *Nanaloricus mysticus*, family Nanaloricidae, Order Nanaloricida, and Phylum Loricifera, was collected at 25 to 30 m depth from shelly gravel substrate near Roscoff (N. Brittany) in 1982. (Kristensen, 1983). As they have subsequently been found at widely scattered locations (on both sides of the N. Atlantic and in the Coral Sea) but always in similar marine sediments, it is likely that these virtually unknown animals are distributed worldwide and, most probably in British waters.

Phylum NEMATOMORPHA

Adult horse-hair worms look very like a writhing length of coarse hair – extremely long, thin, bi-laterally symmetrical and unsomited. The basic organisation of the body is similar to that of a nematode, although lacking circular muscles. Juveniles are parasitic in arthropods and the free-living adult stage is short-lived, serving only a reproductive function. It is without alimentary, respiratory and excretory systems. The sexes are separate and fertilisation is internal. The eggs hatch into a larval stage, with stylets, which invades the new host. Soil-dwelling or freshwater members of the Order Gordioida, include *Gordius* which parasitises water beetles in Britain.

Order **Nectonematida**: at least one species probably occurs in British waters.
Marine. Adults have a double row of setae along most of the body, used in swimming. *Nectonema munida* parasitises spider crabs (Bourdon, 1965, reported by Ingle, 1996).

Phylum NEMATODA

Round worms are small multicellular worm-shaped organisms which can be found in almost every conceivable environment. Apart from the free-living forms in soil, freshwater and marine benthic habitats, they also parasitise plants and other animals, including man. The whole phylum currently contains some 20,000 nominal species. There are about 4,000 free-living marine forms and some 450 of those, representing 170 genera, have been recorded in British waters. However, the numbers so far recorded are only a small fraction of the probable total. They are also extremely abundant – around 20 million per square metre on some salt marshes. Species richness is atypically high, with 100 species per sandy beach appearing normal.

Most adult nematodes are elongated cylindrical worms, typically tapering at both ends, around 1-2mm in length (although longer ones are to be found in kelp holdfasts). The body is essentially a tube within a tube. The outer tube is the body wall consisting, externally, of a cuticle layer and, internally, of a longitudinal muscle layer. Round worms do not have circular muscles and so are unable to elongate or contract the body. Movement is achieved by alternate contraction of the dorsal and ventral muscle blocks, working against the hydrostatic skeleton. The internal tube is the gut, which is terminal at the front end but subterminal posteriorly, so that nematodes have a tail.

The cuticle bears a number of sensory structures, called sensilla, which have a similar basic structure yet may be long and hair-like (setae) or nipple-like (papillae). Somatic sensilla are found on the general body surface. Those on the tail (caudal sensilla) may be longer and stouter than the rest, and specialised sensilla at the tail tip are called terminal sensilla. The head bears a number of special cephalic sensilla, in addition to two chemosensory amphids – which may be of a pocket-type, transverse slit-type, circular-type or spiral-type with varying numbers of turns.

Most marine species are selective deposit feeders. The sexes are separate, fertilisation is by copulation, and there is direct benthic development of the egg through four juvenile stages to the adult. Although a useful review of marine nematode systematics can be found in Heip *et al.* (1982), the most comprehensive examination of the systematics of free-living nematodes is that of Lorenzen (1981), recently revised and translated into English (Lorenzen, 1994).

Class Secernentea;

Order **Rhabditida**: 2 British marine species.

Most members of this Class are soil-dwelling or parasitic terrestrial species., often having posterior chemosensory organs called phasmids. Only two species of *Rhabditis* (which has some 70 terrestrial forms), have been found free-living in the marine environment – and then only along the strandline. See Platt & Warwick (1983).

Order **Ascaridida**: at least 4 British marine species in a single family.

Adults are parasites of vertebrates, these four species having been recorded from the intestines of various fishes. They have 3-6 lips around the mouth.

Order **Spirurida**: at least 11 British marine species in 3 families.

Adults are typically parasites of vertebrates. Ten of these eleven species were recorded from the stomach or intestines of various fishes; the other, *Philometra grayi*, came from the sea urchin *Echinus esculentus*. Spirurids usually have 2 lips around the mouth (occasionally 0 or 4).

Class Adenophorea

Mainly free living, and without phasmids (chemoreceptory structures at the posterior end of the body). Amphids located posteriorly in the head region. Head and body with sensilla and papillae.

Subclass Enoplia

Order **Enoplida**: 101 British species in 15 families.

Predominantly marine with simple. pouch-like amphids with slit-shaped or ellipsoid apertures. Well-developed cephalic sensilla in three whorls. Body surface smooth or transversely striated. See Platt & Warwick (1983).

Subclass Chromadoria

Order **Chromadorida**: 195 British marine species in 18 families.

Mostly marine, but also soil dwelling and freshwater, with spiral amphids. Well-developed cephalic sensilla in three whorls. Body surface transversely striated. See Platt & Warwick (1988).

Order **Monhysterida**: 93 British marine species in 8 families.

Marine, freshwater and soil-dwelling, with circular to spiral amphids. Second and third whorls of cephalic sensilla combined, or only the third present. Body surface transversely striated. See Warwick & Platt (1997).

Phylum SIPUNCULA

Peanut worms are bilaterally-symmetrical, cylindrical, unsomited, benthic, deposit-feeding marine worms that range in size between 2mm and 70cm. They have an anterior 'introvert' which can be withdrawn within the trunk or extended to a considerable distance away. The mouth, at the end of the introvert, is surrounded by ciliated tentacles, or lobes. Dorsal to the mouth, there is a sensory prominence (called the nuchal organ) that lies over the brain. All movement, even the extension/retraction of the introvert is slow. The gut is 'U'-shaped so that the anus opens dorsally at the base of the introvert. In all but one species, the sexes are separate; fertilisation is external; the eggs hatch as short-lived trochophore larvae. In some species, development is direct thereafter, but in others there is a longer-lived pelagosphaera larva. See Gibbs (1977): Hayward & Ryland (1990; 1995).

Class Phascolosomatidea
Tentacles all lie dorsal to the mouth and form a horseshoe around the nuchal organ.

Order **Aspidosiphonida**: one British species.
Sipunculans with horny epidermal shields at one (or both) ends of the trunk. *Aspidosiphon mulleri* lives in empty gastropod shells, serpulid tubes etc. The anal shield acts as an operculum when the introvert is withdrawn. Animal up to 80mm in length with 10 or 12 short tentacles.

Order **Phascolosomatida**: one British species.
Sipunculans without epidermal shields. *Phascolosoma granulatum* lives in muddy sand and gravel. Animal up to 100mm in length with between 12 and 60 tentacles, increasing with size, all forming a dorsally-opening horseshoe.

Class Sipunculidea
Tentacles surround the mouth, although some dorsal tentacles form a horseshoe around the nuchal organ.

Order **Golfingiida**: 9 British species in two families.
The longitudinal muscles form a single layer within the body and are not split up into bands. Most species live in mud or muddy sand, often in crevices.

Order **Sipunculida**: 2 British species in a single family.
The longitudinal muscles are grouped in bands. Most species live in mud or muddy sand, often in crevices but *Phascolion strombi* lives in discarded gastropod shells into which they wall themselves, leaving a small hole through which the introvert is extended.

Phylum ECHIURA

Gutter worms are bilaterally-symmetrical, unsomited, benthic, deposit-feeding marine worms with a bulbous or cylindrical body form. British species range in size between 20 to 180mm. They have a highly extensible (but not eversible) anterior proboscis, which is the food collecting and gaseous exchange organ. The long coiled gut extends from the mouth, at the base of the proboscis, to the terminal anus. The sexes are separate, fertilisation is mainly external, the eggs hatch as trochophore larvae. The group is not divided into Classes although four Orders (two of which occur in the Atlantic) are recognised. See Stephen (1960): Hayward & Ryland (1990; 1995).

Order **Echiurida**: 3 British species in a single family.
   Both sexes are of a similar size. The animals have at least one pair of anteroventral chaetae: some have posterior chaetae as well.

Order **Bonelliida**: 3 British species in a single family.
   The dwarf males are parasitic on the (much larger) females. Some lack chaetae altogether and none have posterior chaetae.

Phylum POGONOPHORA

Beard worms are threadlike marine animals of sedentary habit, living in distinctive chitinous tubes. The bilaterally symmetrical body consists of four regions: a small protosoma furnished with the cephalic lobe and between 1 and 10 very long ciliated tentacles; a longer mesosoma; and a very long metasoma. There is no mouth, alimentary canal or anus. They gain organic carbon from internal symbiotic bacteria which, in turn, use such compounds as sulphides and methane translocated from the surrounding sediment. For this reason, their burrows straddle the redox potential discontinuity layer between oxic and anoxic sediments. The sexes are separate but show no sexual dimorphism, fertilisation is external to the body but within the tube and there is no free larval stage and, therefore, no metamorphosis in the life cycle.

   Most Pogonophora live at great depth but a few species are now known from the European shelf, slope and fjords and *Siboglinum fiordicum* has been recorded in sediment at a depth of 25m. The phylum comprises some 100 living species. See Ivanov (1963), Hayward & Ryland (1990).

Class Frenulatea

Order **Athecanephrida**: 7 British species in 2 families.
   Excretory portions of the anterior coelomoducts are widely separated, each adjoining the lateral cephalic blood vessel. Either with one tentacle, in the genus *Siboglinum*, or 7 in the species *Oligobrachia ivanovi*.

Order **Thecanephridia**: 2 British species in 2 families.
   Excretory portions of the anterior coelomoducts are close to each other, almost median. With 2, 3 or 4 tentacles.

Phylum ANNELIDA

Annelids are distinguished from all other worm-shaped animals by the possession of an elongated, bilaterally symmetrical, soft body divided (sometimes incompletely) by transverse septa into a series of more or less similar somites[18]. They use their fluid-filled body cavity (coelom) as a hydrostatic skeleton, on which the muscles of the body wall act to contract or elongate the body. Traction with the substratum is increased, in most species, by somitally-arranged bristles (chaetae) protruding through the body wall. Nerves, blood vessels and excretory organs are metamerically (somitally-) arranged, but the gut tends to be a straight tube running the whole length of the body.

Class Polychaeta

It is difficult to cite a suite of morphological characters which completely separates all polychaetes from all other annelid groups. The word means "many bristles" and most species have somitally-arranged lateral fleshy lobes (parapodia) bearing numerous chaetae – but the lobes are not always obvious nor are the chaetae always numerous. Polychaetes typically have chaetae of different types in different regions of their bodies. The sexes are typically separate. Eggs typically develop into a free-swimming trochophore larva.

The elongated, often cylindrical, body can be subdivided into four zones: presomital prostomium and peristomium, a large number of trunk somites and the post somital pygidium, bearing the anus. As the animal grows, new trunk somites are added in an area just anterior to the pygidium. In the more advanced groups, a process of cephalisation has incorporated some of the anterior trunk somites into an enhanced head region. They are mainly free-living but some are commensal and, a very few, parasitic. The body form varies widely, reflecting a range of habitats from pelagic, through crawling with occasional swimming, to active burrowing and inactive tube dwelling.

The 8,000, or so, species are grouped into some 80 families; almost all of them are marine (all of the British species are). Six of these contain planktonic species but most are benthic animals for most of their lives. It has been difficult for taxonomists to agree a classification above family level, and for years the families have been regarded as Errantia or Sedentaria on the basis of their life style. In the *Synopses of the British Fauna*, however, a system of Orders and Superfamilies has been adopted. The Polychaeta are to be covered by 11 volumes, 4 of which had been published by the end of 1997. There are around 540 species in 76 families. Keys[19] to the Orders are printed in Synopses No. 32, No. 45, No. 54 and will be included in subsequent volumes. Until the series is complete the best general keys to British genera are those Hayward & Ryland (1990; 1995), and the illustrations in Hayward *et al.* (1996), although neither includes interstitial forms.

---

[18] Somite or segment? There is confusion of terminology in the literature. Some authors use the word 'segment' for the body somites of, for example, a worm or a shrimp. Others use it for the sections of arthropod appendages. I have tried to follow the latter convention and use 'somite' for the replicated sections of the body.

[19] These keys are more complete than the relevant section of Key 7 herein and so was incorporated in the test version. Testers, however, found it difficult for beginners to use – even for the easily-recognised species. Key 5 has, accordingly, been re-written with the inexperienced in mind but is no longer complete.

Order **Phyllodocida**: 214 British species in 28 families.

Errant polychaetes, active predators or scavengers, having a muscular cylindrical pharynx (proboscis) armed with 0 - 2 pairs of jaws. Prostomium with one or more pairs of antennae. Well developed parapodia with aciculae. The Order includes ragworms, catworms, paddleworms, scale worms etc. There are 11 Superfamilies. Pleijel & Dales (1991) cover 3 of them – Phyllodocoidea (50 species in 3 families), Typhloscolecoidea (3 species in 1 family) and Tomopteroidea (4 species in 1 family). Chambers & Muir (1997) cover 3 more – Chrysopetaloidea, Pisionoidea and Aphroditoidea.

Order **Amphinomida**: 6 British species in 2 families.

Prostomium with three to five pairs of antennae and a posterior caruncle. Anterior somites encroach around and enclose the prostomium and peristomium. The cylindrical, rasping pad-like proboscis is without papillae or jaws. Some of the parapodia bear gills. Most amphinomids are carnivores of sponges, hydroids or ascidians. See George & Hartmann-Schröder (1985).

Order **Spintherida**: 4 British species in 1 family.

The body is short, oval, and dorso-ventrally flattened. The tiny prostomium is dominated by a single antenna, and typically bears 4 eyes. The anterior somites encroach around and in front of the prostomium and peristomium. Notopodia are extended into transverse dorsal ridges. Pharynx eversible forming a voluminous rosette-like sac, without jaws. Most spintherids are carnivores or ectoparasites of sponges or hydroids, and are typically of the same colour as their hosts. See George & Hartmann-Schröder (1985).

Order **Eunicida**: 58 British species in 10 families.

Most eunicids are active errant polychaetes. They are predators, scavengers, or parasites having an extremely muscular cylindrical ventrally-eversible pharynx (proboscis) armed with a complicated jaw mechanism (reduced in some forms). Prostomium with or without appendages. The Order includes some interstitial worms, and an aberrant parasite of lobsters, *Histriobdella homari*. See George & Hartmann-Schröder (1985).

Order **Orbiniida**: 14 British species in 2 families.

The elongate body, with numerous somites, is indistinctly divided into a dorso-ventrally flattened anterior section and a cylindrical posterior part. Finger-like, dorsal gills. Soft, sac-like proboscis. Head without any prostomial appendages or palps.

Order **Spionida**: 52 British species in 7 families.

Small to medium-sized worms. Head with a pair (or two groups) of longitudinally-grooved palps on the peristomium, but without jaws. Typically without any prostomial appendages (although sometimes there is an occipital antenna).

Order **Ctenodrilida**: 1 family.

Very small interstitial worms with few somites. No prostomial appendages, palps, gills or parapodial lobes. With a few simple chaetae arising directly from the body wall.

Order **Psammodrilida**: 2 British species in 1 family.
Small (1 or 6mm), grub-shaped, interstitial worms, without prostomial appendages or palps, that have several somites in the middle of their body with elongate notopodia supported by aciculae. Apart from these, parapodial lobes are absent. Almost completely ciliated. See Westheide (1990).

Order **Cossurida**: 1 family.
Thread-like worms of numerous similar somites, with a single medial dorsal tentacle arising on somite 4, 5, 6, or 7, often almost as long as the body. Parapodia biramous, but with very low lobes. Without prostomial appendages.

Order **Flabelligerida**: 6 British species in 2 families.
Prostomium reduced and fused to the peristomium, and retractable into the rest of the body. Body surface papillated and not divided into regions. Parapodia biramous with reduced lobes. Pharynx unarmed: non-eversible. Blood often contains chlorocruorin, giving the animal an unusual greenish colour.

Order **Sternaspida**: 1 family.
Short, broad worms with few somites. The first three bear rows of stout chaetae. The posteroventral region has a stiff, mineralised, chitinous shield. Posterior gills.

Order **Capitellida**: 36 British species in 3 families.
Elongate, cylindrical worms with an eversible, thin-walled proboscis. Parapodia poorly-developed, without acicula or cirri. They are always biramous with some notopodia forming transverse ridges. Head without prostomial appendages or palps.

Order **Opheliida**: 16 British species in 2 families.
Short bodied, cylindrical, often annular, worms with an eversible thin walled proboscis. Head without prostomial appendages or palps. Short truncate neuropodia bear finely tapering chaetae on all but the first somite. They sometimes have cylindrical lateral gills.

Order **Nerillida**: 16 British species in 1 family.
Minute (<1.5mm) interstitial worms with few, transparent somites – body comprising prostomium, 7-9 trunk somites and the pygidium, which typically has 2 anal cirri. First (buccal) somite may be without chaetae. See Westheide (1990).

Order **Dinophilida**: 4 British species in 1 family.
Minute (<2.5mm), cigar-shaped worms that may be extremely abundant in intertidal muds. A slight neck present between the broad, rounded prostomium and the trunk. No fleshy prostomial or parapodial appendages and no chaetae. There are transverse ciliary rings around at least part of the body. See Westheide (1990).

Order **Polygordiida**: 2 British species in 1 family.
Slender thread-like worms, up to 10cm long, with a cylindrical body composed of many similar somites that are poorly (or not at all) visible externally. Surface extremely smooth and somewhat iridescent. No parapodia or chaetae. Two, stiff, forward-facing tentacles on the prostomium. See Westheide (1990).

Order **Protodrilida**: 13 British species in 3 families.
Body elongate, thread-like, multisomited with or without rudimentary parapodia and chaetae. Gliding locomotion achieved by a ventral ciliary band. Head with two mobile, flexible tentacles (palps). Two eyes. See Westheide (1990).

Order **Oweniida**: 2 British species in 1 family.
Tube-dwelling in a sandy tube. Worm with a few elongate somites, some rather indistinct and indicated only be their chaetae. Prostomium fused to peristomium, often with lobes or frills. Dense field of neuropodial hooks.

Order **Terebellida**: 48 British species in 5 families.
Tube dwelling, typically in a sandy tube. Prostomium without appendages, peristomium with, typically long, feeding tentacles. Body divided into three regions and with one or more pair(s) of gills at the anterior end.

Order **Sabellida**: 43 British species in 3 families.
Tube dwelling in mud tubes (Sabellidae) or in sinuous (Serpulidae) or coiled (Spirorbidae) calcareous tubes cemented to a firm substrate. Prostomium reduced and fused with the peristomium, forming a stiff tentacular crown. Body divided into two regions, the neuropodial and notopodial chaetal types reversing at the transition.

Class Myzostomata

Order **Myzostomida**: 1 British species.
Flat, disc shaped animals without a distinct head, pygidium or any external signs of somitation apart from the 10 pairs of uniramous parapodia, each with one hooked chaeta, alternating with sucker-like organs along the body. There is a muscular pharynx which can be protruded from the front end. Parasites or commensals of echinoderms, especially crinoids, and thus all marine. *Myzostoma cirriferum* (>4mm in length) is an ectoparasite of the feather star *Antedon bifida*.

Class Clitellata

Head without appendages. Body without parapodia, and with few or no chaetae, but typically with a glandular area of skin (clitellum) which secretes a cocoon within which the fertilised eggs are enclosed. The worms are hermaphrodite, with cross fertilisation via copulatory organs. No larval stages.

Subclass Oligochaeta

It is also difficult to cite a suit of morphological characters which completely separates all oligochaetes from all other annelid groups. The word means 'few bristles' and these are typically somitally-arranged, in bunches (although there may be only one or two in a bunch). The body is without terminal suckers. Oligochaetes are characteristic of terrestrial and freshwater habitats.

Order **Haplotaxida**

Suborder Tubificina: 71 British marine and estuarine species in 3 families.
Marine and estuarine species belong to the families Naididae, Enchytraeidae and Tubificidae – all of which have relatives in the other habitats – and only the last-named has offshore representatives. Many of the others are really freshwater animals which

just penetrate brackish habitats. Reproduction is frequently asexual, particularly in naidids. See Brinkhurst (1982).

Subclass Hirudinoida

Leeches always have a posterior sucker, and many also have an anterior one. Body of 30 somites, but they always appear to have many more as each is divided up by some 3-5 annuli (range 2-14). Chaetae are always lacking from all but the anterior somites. Predators or parasites in fresh water, in the sea and on the land. About one fifth of all leech species live in salt or brackish water – almost all of which belong to the family Piscicolidae (which also has a freshwater species in Britain).

Order **Rhynchobdellida**: 22 British marine species in 1 family.

These leeches (in the family Piscicolidae) are without chaetae and without jaws. The pharynx forms a muscular contractile proboscis. There is an anterior sucker present, as well as the back one. Ancestral piscicolids live in the buccal cavity of their hosts. Others start off there and then move out onto the body surface, especially at the base of the fins, as they grow. Rock pool fishes show a higher percentage infestation in NE than in SW England (Hussain & Knight-Jones, 1995). In addition to the 22 reliably recorded in British waters, there are several others, parasites of North Atlantic fishes, which might appear here in due course. See Hayward & Ryland (1990): Hussain & Knight-Jones (1995).

Phylum MOLLUSCA

The second largest Phylum in the Animal Kingdom. With approximately 100,000 living species, molluscs include the animals popularly known as snails, slugs, mussels, clams, squids and cuttlefish – as well as many others less well known. They range in size from a few mm in length to several metres: giant squids are the largest living invertebrates. They are unsomited, essentially free-living animals whose bodies are covered by a sheet of skin (the mantle) which, in most species, secretes an external, protective, calcareous shell of from one to eight plates. In some species the shell is now internal, in others it is absent. In two, presumably primitive, Classes the shell is represented by a multiplicity of calcareous spicules. Locomotion generally depends on a broad muscular creeping foot, which may be modified for burrowing or swimming.

The most primitive groups may have been hermaphrodite, releasing gametes into the sea where fertilisation took place externally, but there is an evolutionary trend towards single-sex individuals and internal fertilisation. Primitively, the zygote developed into a trochophore larva similar to that of a worm but in more advanced forms the trochophore stage is short-lived (or lost) and a veliger larva is the important swimming stage. In still others, the veliger stage takes place within an egg capsule from which a 'miniature adult' hatches.

Taylor (1996) considers the relationships between the major groups.

Some 846 species may be considered British (Smith & Heppell, 1991, omitting their deep-water species).

Class Caudofoveata

A small group of shell-less, burrowing, worm-shaped molluscs, up to about 80mm in length, regarded as representing the earliest offshoot within the phylum, quite distinct from the remaining molluscan Classes. The bilaterally-symmetrical cylindrical body is encased in a chitinous cuticle, covered with calcareous spicules. There are no eyes or tentacles, and no definite head, so that the two ends of the body are hard to distinguish. There is no ventral furrow (*cf.* Class Solenogastres) and the foot is represented by a small shield around the mouth, which collects food and passes it to the radula. There is a pair of bipectinate gills at the extreme posterior end. Sexes are separate and fertilisation is external. Larval development is unknown.

Adults live, head down, in vertical burrows, with their expanded gills at the entrance. They probably feed on micro-organisms and organic matter although they do not ingest unsorted sediment. They are exclusively marine, subtidal, and apparently world-wide in distribution. The three British species, from two families, are found in soft muddy /sandy sediments at densities of up to 3 per square metre and from 8 – 900m depth, although most are found between 20 and 115m. See Jones & Baxter (1987) and Salvini-Plawen (1985).

Class Solenogastres

A small group of shell-less, worm-shaped molluscs living on the mud surface or on hydroids, corals or other cnidaria on which they feed. Generally small, up to about 100mm but most less than 50mm in length; regarded as closer to the shell-bearing molluscs than the Caudofoveata, with which they were once grouped. The bilaterally-symmetrical, laterally-compressed, body lacks a definite head, so that the two ends of the body are hard to distinguish. A mid-dorsal longitudinal crest or keel is often present. The ventral surface has a median longitudinal groove (ventral furrow), part of which represents the molluscan foot. The rest of the body is covered by a complex cuticle bearing one or several layers of calcareous spicules or, in *Tegulaherpia celtica*, scales. Bipectinate gills (*cf.* Caudofoveata) are absent but the cloaca may contain secondary lamellar 'gills'.

The animals are simultaneous hermaphrodites, but normally copulate and cross-fertilise. Larval development is presumed to include a planktonic phase.

The group is exclusively marine and most individuals remain subtidal, from shallow water to considerable depths, although *Lepidomenia hystrix* has been recorded from the shore in Strangford Lough, Northern Ireland. See Jones & Baxter (1987) and Caudwell, Jones & Killeen (1995).

Order **Pholidoskepia**: 5 British species in 3 families.
Nematonemia species, family Dondersiidae, are greyish-red worm-like animals up to 30mm long but less than 1mm in breadth. They live, at depths below 45m., entwined amongst the branches of hydroid colonies (e.g., the Leptothecatae *Lafoea dumosa* and *Grammaria abietina*) on which they are presumed to feed. Most other species are less than 5mm long and are regarded as meiofaunal, feeding carnivorously on Cnidaria, although *Lepidomenia* species are associated with the solitary coral *Balanophyllia*.

Order **Neomeniamorpha**: 2 British species in a single family.
The sluggish *Neomenia* species are normally found buried vertically, head down, in the mud. British forms reach about 30mm in length and are found at depths exceeding 18m.

Order **Cavibelonia**: 4 British species in 3 families.
Yellowish-white or yellowish-grey worm-like animals, up to 35mm long but typically much smaller, apparently restricted in distribution to colonies of leptothecate hydroids of the family Aglaopheniidae, especially *Lytocarpa myriophyllum*, at depths in excess of 50m.

Class Polyplacophora

Chitons, or coat-of-mail shells, are a small, ancient, group of elongate/oval, dorsoventrally-flattened, bilaterally-symmetrical molluscs, having a dorsal shell composed of 8, transverse, serially-overlapping plates embedded in, and sometimes covered by, a girdle. There is a large, muscular, ventral foot but the poorly-differentiated head is without eyes or tentacles. Although exotic species may reach 300mm in length, British representatives rarely exceed 60mm and most are less than 40mm. Chitons occur from the mid-littoral down to 400m, but are mainly animals of the lower littoral and shallow sublittoral.

Sexes are separate, fertilisation is external (both eggs and sperm being released into the seawater) and the, typically planktonic, trochophore larva develops directly into a juvenile. There is no veliger stage.

Although conspicuous members of the littoral and sub-littoral fauna in many parts of the world, the 11 (possibly 12) British species are small, drab and inconspicuous. All are grazer/browsers of the rock surface, crawling on their broad muscular foot and scraping up organic matter with their radula. Fish and crabs are the main predators. Jones & Baxter (1987), group the British species into 3 Orders within the Subclass Neoloricata, as below, whilst Smith & Heppell (1991) demote Neoloricata to an Order.

Order **Lepidopleurina**: 8 British species in 2 families.
Containing the most primitive of living chitons. The outer edges of the shell valves are without attachment teeth. The girdle is narrow and does not extend over the valves. Only a few pairs of gills are present, at the back end near the anus.

Order **Ischnochitonina**: 6 British species in a single family.
The outer edges of the shell valves have attachment teeth. The girdle varies in relative width and in ornamentation but does not encroach to any extent over the plates. Gills occupy most of the mantle groove, except near the anus.

Order **Acanthochitonina**: 2 British species in a single family.
The outer edges of the shell valves have attachment teeth. The girdle encroaches over the valves, either partially of completely, often bearing tufts of bristles. Only a few pairs of gills are present, along part of the mantle groove.

Class Gastropoda

Slugs and snails form a large group of essentially asymmetrical molluscs (although some slugs have secondarily developed external bi-lateral symmetry). Most gastropods have a single, often spirally-coiled, shell into which the body can be withdrawn – although this has been reduced or lost in some forms. During development, the visceral mass and the mantle (together with the shell it has secreted) rotates through 180°, relative to the head and foot, to bring the mantle cavity anterior. The head bears tentacles, eyes, jaws and radula: whilst locomotion depends on a broad muscular foot – sometimes modified for burrowing or swimming. Mainly marine, but with terrestrial and freshwater species in Britain.

The higher classification of gastropods is, once again, the subject of considerable modification and debate. Hayward & Ryland (1990) and Smith & Heppell (1991) adopt a traditional view, but the work of Ponder & Warén, 1988), Haszprunar (1988), Healy, (1988), Lindberg (1988), and Hickman (1988) really set taxonomists thinking. The scheme that follows is the author's synthesis of ideas put forward during the Centenary Symposium of the Malacological Society of London (on the Origin and Evolutionary Radiation of the Mollusca) in September 1993.

Subclass Prosobranchia

Prosobranchs always have a shell, which almost always is external. The animal typically has an operculum. The head has a single pair of tentacles, each bearing an eye at its base. The sexes are typically separate. There is frequently a planktonic dispersal phase in the life cycle – either free-floating eggs or a veliger larva (or both). Almost all species are marine but there are a few terrestrial and some freshwater representatives. See Graham (1988).

For much of this century, Prosobranchs were been divided between three Orders – Archaeogastropoda, Mesogastropoda and Neogastropoda (Thiele, 1925) – but a synthesis of Hickman (1988), Lindberg (1988), Ponder & Warén (1988), and their updates, suggests the following.

Super-Order Patellogastropoda (sensu Lindberg, 1988): 9 British species in 4 families
Limpets are epifaunal grazing herbivores/ detritivores. All have an imperforate, conical, external shell without any trace of helical coiling below the protoconch. The operculum is lost on metamorphosis from the veliger larva. These animals are protandrous hermaphrodites, or the sexes are separate, with external fertilisation – the male does not have a penis.

Super-Order Archaeogastropoda (sensu Hickman, 1988)
Order **Vetigastropoda**: 31 British marine species in 7 families.
Shell with a nacreous layer. Radula with numerous teeth in a transverse row. Sexes typically separate with external fertilisation – the male does not have a penis. Typically, with a pair of bi-pectinate gills in the mantle cavity, the edges of which do not fuse to form a siphon. Many species retain the ancestral fringe of tentacles on the mantle. Members of the Superfamilies Pleurotomariacea Haliotidacea and Fissurellacea have perforate shells – that is, waste water leaves the mantle cavity through a slit (or through one or more holes) in the shell. Many of these animals resemble limpets and do not have an operculum after the larval stage. The fourth Superfamily, Trochacea, (topshells and their allies) have helically-coiled shells and a circular operculum.

Vetigastropods are surface-living (epifaunal) grazing herbivores (mainly of red algae) or detritivores.

Order **Cocculiniformia**: 1 British species.
Lepetella laterocompressa is a small (1.5mm), limpet-like animal whose shell shows no
trace of a spire or spiral coiling. It is found only in deep water between Shetland and
Norway. Dantart & Luque (1994) review the species found off Spanish coasts, some
of which may extend further north.

Super-Order Caenogastropoda
The more advanced Prosobranchs, all probably derived from an Archaeogastropod
ancestor.

Order **Architaenioglossa**: 3 British species. Both species of *Viviparus* are freshwater animals.
Acicula fusca is terrestrial.

Order **Neotaenioglossa**
Shell without a nacreous layer. Radula with 7 teeth in each transverse row. Sexes
separate with internal fertilisation – male has a penis. One (left) mono-pectinate gill in
the mantle cavity, the edges of which may fuse to form a siphon.

Suborder Discopoda: 96 British marine species in 24 families.
The shell is external in all British genera except *Lamellaria*. Most species have an
operculum, but this is absent in cowries, and related forms, Super-family
Lamellariacea, in which lobes of the mantle cover the shell of an active animal. In
pelican's foot shells, Aporrhaidae, the outer lip of the shell aperture is drawn out into
a plate shaped like the webbed foot of a bird. They are infaunal deposit feeders but
most members of this Suborder are surface-living (epifaunal) grazing herbivores or
detritivores. However, calyptraeaceans are filter feeders. Members of the families
Triviidae, Ovulidae and Lamellariidae are epifaunal carnivores of ascidians,
bryozoans, hydroids or soft corals. Moon shells, Naticidae, are infaunal burrowing
carnivores of bivalves (mainly tellins).

Suborder Heteropoda: 3 British species.
Heteropods, e.g., *Carinaria lamarcki* are pelagic carnivores with a reduced shell, and
without an operculum as an adult.

Suborder Ptenoglossa: 46 British marine species, in 6 families.
Species of the Eulimidae are ectoparasites of echinoderms, mostly of sea cucumbers
and brittle stars, although *Pelseneeria stilifera* lives on sea urchins. No British species is
endoparasitic. Members of the pelagic carnivorous family, Janthinidae, are without an
operculum in the adult. Many species in this Suborder are hermaphrodite.

Order **Neogastropoda**: 49 British species, all marine, in 5 families.
Shell without a nacreous layer. Radula with 1-3 teeth in each transverse row. Sexes
separate, although some may be consecutive hermaphrodites, with internal fertilisation
– the male has a penis. One (left) mono-pectinate gill in the mantle cavity, the edges
of which fuse to form a siphon, protected at the base by the shell's siphonal canal. The
shell is external in all British species. Most are surface-living (epifaunal) specialised
carnivores.

Subclass Heterobranchia

In contrast to all other molluscan taxa (except the Solenogastres) most members of this Subclass are hermaphrodite (99% of genera world-wide). Indeed, this may be their most obvious linking character. See Heller (1993).

Order **Heterostropha**: 61 British marine species in 3 families.

A group of four Super-families: Valvatoidea; (all 3 British species are freshwater snails); Rissoellacea (3 British species); Omalogyracea (2 British species); and Pyramidellacea (56 British species). All are regarded, in one way or another, as intermediate between Prosobranchs and Opisthobranchs. All have external shells and opercula. All are hermaphrodite. Pyramidellids are surface-living ectoparasites associated with particular hosts, often a serpulid polychaete or a bivalve mollusc (especially a scallop, mussel or oyster), but including bryozoans and a starfish.

Infra-Class Euthyneura

The most advanced group of gastropods.

Super-Order Opisthobranchia

In opisthobranch molluscs, the precarious balance between hard and soft parts is markedly tilted in favour of the latter. The shell is typically reduced, internal or absent, and the post-larval animal is, almost always, without an operculum. Where the shell is absent, the animal is free to assume all kinds of flamboyant shapes, complementing a wide range of epifaunal lifestyles. The body typically appears bilaterally symmetrical, with a distinct head bearing up to four pairs of tentacles (although all may be absent in burrowing forms which have developed a large flattened cephalic shield). Sea-slugs are hermaphrodite with internal fertilisation, copulation being normally reciprocal. The spawn is typically jelly-like and, in most species, the eggs hatch into shelled (and often operculate), planktonic, veliger larvae. Longevity, of British species, is typically one year or less. Marine or estuarine in distribution. See Thompson (1988).

Order **Cephalaspidea**: 27 British species in 8 families.

Bubble shells are often burrowing (infaunal) carnivores feeding on foraminiferans, polychaetes or bivalves (*Acteon, Scaphander, Philine* etc.), sometimes attacking relatively fast-moving prey (*Retusa*) or, more rarely, general browsers (*Runcina*) or herbivores (*Haminea*). In some species, the sides of the foot are expanded into parapodial lobes which may be used for swimming. Shell external (14 species), internal (9 species) or absent (4 species) in the adult. Only *Acteon tornatilis*, retains the operculum in the adult stage. Mikkelsen (1994) examined the relationships within the order, and discussed its phylogeny.

Order **Acochlidioidea**: 8 British species in 3 families.

Minute (up to 4mm long, but most only 2mm) interstitial (meiofaunal) shell-less slugs, presumably feeding on micro-organisms.

Order **Sacoglossa**: 10 British species in 3 families.

Surface-living (epifaunal) specialist herbivores, feeding principally on green algae. Shell absent in the adult stage.

Order **Anaspidea**: 5 British species in 2 families.

Sea hares are surface-living (epifaunal) herbivores or omnivores. The sides of the foot are expanded into substantial parapodial lobes which may be used for swimming. Shell external (*Akera bullata*) and visible although the animal may be unable to retract completely within it, or internal (3 species of Aplysia) in the adult.

Order **Notaspidea**: 4 British species in 1 family.

Surface-living (epifaunal) carnivores, feeding principally on ascidians. *Pleurobranchus membranaceus* is an active swimmer, but the other species are entirely benthic. Shell internal in the adult, and about half the body length.

Order **Thecosomata**: 19 British species in 4 families.

Shelled pteropods are planktonic filter feeders. Parapodial lobes of the foot form large wing-like fins. Head tentacles are well-developed, with wing tentacles also in some species. The external shell may be calcareous (helically coiled or a more-or-less straight cone), a transparent cartilaginous pseudoconch, or absent. The operculum is typically absent in the adult stage (Spoel, 1967; 1972; 1976).

Order **Gymnosomata**: 21 British species in 5 families.

Naked pteropods are specialised planktonic predators of shelled pteropods, with small ventral parapodial fins and lacking both shell and operculum. Head with two pairs of tentacles. Body with a marked 'waist'. Anterior gut with adhesive cones, arms or hooked structures protrusable through the mouth (Morton, 1957: Spoel, 1976).

Order **Nudibranchia**: 121 British species in 33 families.

The true sea slugs, typically with numerous dorsal finger-like projections (cerata), are mostly surface-living (epifaunal) carnivores of sedentary animals – ascidians, bryozoans, entoprocts, sponges, hydroids, sea anemones and soft corals. Some are apparently species-specific. *Pseudovermis* is an interstitial carnivore of burrowing anemones. Pelagic species feed on goose barnacles and *Velella*. Shell absent in the adult stage.

Super-Order Pulmonata

Terrestrial slugs and snails (Order Stylommatophora) and pond snails (Order Basommatophora) are outside the scope of this key but there are a few intertidal marine and estuarine pulmonates which must be included.

Order **Archaeopulmonata**: 3 British marine species in 2 families.

Ellobiid and otinid snails are always shelled. The single pair of head tentacles can be retracted but not invaginated (turned inside-out): eyes are at the base of the tentacles. Although hermaphrodite, when pairing, an individual acts either as a male or as a female. Some species are self fertile. There are no free-living larval stages. The mantle cavity forms a lung with a contractile opening, called the pneumostome, behind the head on the right-hand side. There is no operculum. *Otina otis* lives in the littoral fringe of exposed rocky shores in Southwest Britain whilst *Phytia myosotis* and *Leucophytia bidentata* are found primarily on salt marshes. Traditionally, these have been included in the Order Basommatophora, but support for this separate Order is increasing.

Order **Systelommatophora**: one British species.
Intertidal slugs of the family Onchidellidae, which show a combination of opisthobranch and pulmonate features, were typically included with terrestrial slugs in the Stylommatophora (when mentioned at all!). *Onchidella celtica*, found intertidally amongst mussels and barnacles on Cornish coasts, is an inconspicuous dark slug reaching some 13 x 6mm in size. The head bears a single pair of short cylindrical tentacles, with eyes at their tips. The thick warty, charcoal grey, mantle (to which sand grains may adhere) extends on each side beyond the, pale grey, foot and covers the head when the animal retracts. The mantle cavity opens posteriorly so that both pneumostome and anus are at the hind end of the body, high up under the 'eaves' of the mantle. A veliger larval stage (complete with shell and operculum) is completed within the egg capsule.

Class Scaphopoda

Tusk shells form a small, distinctive, group of molluscs, having an elongated tubular shell, up to 150mm long, open at both ends. Tusk shells combine features of both Gastropods and Bivalves. The univalve shell and a buccal mass, with a radula, are characteristic of the former whilst the digging foot, lack of a true head (no eyes) and a fused mantle, open at both ends suggest the latter.

They are entirely marine, and exclusively infaunal organisms, living in mud, sand, or gravel from the shallow sub-littoral (3m) down to depths greater than 3,000m. They burrow into the surface layer of the substrate, with the concave surface of the shell uppermost and the posterior tip protruding.

Sexes are separate, fertilisation external (both eggs and sperm being released into the seawater) and the trochophore larva develops via a planktonic veliger larva to the benthic adult.

Generally regarded as carnivores, some scaphopods may be omnivorous. Food is captured by the captaculae and passed back to the mouth along a ciliated tract. The 7 British species are small (3mm to about 40mm long) with white shells, sometimes dark-stained. See Jones & Baxter (1987).

Order **Dentalioidea**: 2 British species in a single family.
With numerous thin captaculae and a substantial burrowing foot, protactile, conical-tipped and with expandable lateral lobes.

Order **Siphonodentalioidea**: 2 British species in separate families.
With few large, broad, captaculae and the foot reduced to a long filiform process, with the lateral lobes forming a frilled disc.

Class Bivalvia

Mussels, clams and their allies have a bilaterally-symmetrical, laterally compressed body enclosed within two calcareous, lateral, shell valves, hinged dorsally by an elastic ligament and aligned by interlocking shell 'teeth'. There are typically two adductor muscles pulling the valves closed, antagonistic to the ligament. The posterior edges of the large mantle cavity are sometimes fused to form siphons (mainly in burrowing forms). The single, typically very large, pair of gills is used for filter-feeding in all but the Protobranchs and Septibranchs. The head is reduced, without eyes, tentacles or radula. Sexes are typically separate; fertilisation is external. Eggs hatch as veliger larvae, typically planktonic. Adults benthic, sedentary on the surface or burrowing within it. Some species can swim. All are aquatic planctivores or detritivores. Most are marine. The grouping of genera into families, and thence into superfamilies is generally accepted, but only recently (e.g., Smith & Heppell, 1991) has this process been acceptably extended to Orders.

Super-Order **Protobranchia**
Order **Nuculoida**: 13 British species, in 2 families.

Nut shells (superfamilies Nuculacea and Nuculanacea) have small, equivalve (the two parts of the shell are approximate mirror images of each other), triangular-elliptical shells. There are numerous small hinge teeth (taxodont condition) arranged in a row on either side of the ligament and equal-sized adductor muscles. Gills are small and used only for breathing; it is the very large palps that are used for food collection. The large burrowing foot has a flat ventral surface. The shell shows no sign of a pallial sinus. Nut shells are all presumed to be deposit-feeding detritivores.

Super-Order **Lamellibranchia**
Order **Arcoida**:
Superfamily Arcacea: 4 British species, in 2 families.

Arc shells have rather heavy, equivalve but inequilateral, boat-shaped shells. The taxodont hinge teeth are arranged in a long straight line. The broad umbones are inrolled. Both adductor muscles are of equal size. They are filter feeders, living low on the shore and sub-littorally attached, by a massive green byssus to the empty shells of other molluscs or in rock crevices. The shell bears a small notch on the side opposite the hinge line to take the byssus.

Superfamily Limopsacea: 1 British species.

The dog-cockle, *Glycymeris glycymeris*, has an almost circular equivalve, equilateral, taxodont shell with a sculpture of fine concentric radiating lines. The animal is an inactive shallow burrowing filter feeder.

Order **Mytiloida**:
Superfamily Mytilacea: 15 British species, in a single family.

Mussels have wedge or fan-shaped equivalve inequilateral shells with the hinge teeth reduced or absent. The anterior adductor muscle is greatly reduced. The periostracum (outer layer of the shell) is often thick, strong oh hairy. The siphons barely extend beyond the end of the shell valves. Filter feeders. Foot can be rolled into a tube to secrete the byssus threads by which the animal is anchored to the rock.

Order **Pterioida**:
Superfamily Pteriacea: 1 British species.

The wing oyster *Pteria hirundo*, lives partially buried in mixed substrata, anchored by byssus threads, via the anterior ventral gape. The brittle inequivalve inequilateral shell is extended into 'wings' along the hinge line. Anterior adductor muscle absent. Filter feeder. Foot small. Sub-littoral.

Superfamily Pinnacea: 1 British species.

The fan mussel, *Pinna fragilis*, is the largest British bivalve, with a thin brittle paddle-shaped shell exceeding 30cm in length. Anterior adductor muscle much smaller than the posterior. The ventral margin of the shell has a long narrow gape for protrusion of the byssus. The animal lives partially buried in mixed substrata, anchored by byssus threads to small stones or pieces of shell.

Order **Limoida**
Superfamily Limacea: 7 British species in a single family.

File shells resemble elongated scallops and, like them, some are able to swim by snapping the valves together. *Lima hians*, probably the best-known of the British species, exposes long fringes of red and orange tentacles whilst swimming "which present a most beautiful sight as they rise and fall about the shell" (Tebble, 1966). It has the unusual habit of darning debris together with its byssus to make a nest among kelp holdfasts, leaving holes for the entrance and exit of water currents.

Order **Ostreoida**:
Superfamily Ostreacea: 4 British species, in a single family.

Only *Ostrea edulis* is truly native: the other oysters were introduced for cultivation. Shell valves dissimilar, with the left (lower) valve cemented to the substratum. There are few or no hinge teeth and the anterior adductor muscle is reduced or absent. Filter feeding sequential hermaphrodites, with a small foot.

Superfamily Pectinacea: 14 British species in a single family.

Scallops have brilliantly-coloured shells that are generally circular or oval in outline. Typically, they live on the bottom, with the cup-shaped right valve underneath and the flatter left valve uppermost. Juveniles are attached by a byssus but, whilst some species become more firmly attached with age, others become free-living and may even swim by snapping the shell. There are few or no hinge teeth and the anterior adductor muscle is reduced or absent. Filter feeders. Foot small. Some scallops are simultaneous hermaphrodites.

Superfamily Anomiacea: 4 British species, in a single family.

Saddle oysters live on hard surfaces, attached by a plug (a calcified byssus) which passes from the inside of the left (upper) valve through a hole in the right (lower) valve. The ligament is internal, attached along the hinge line. No hinge teeth. The upper valve often shows an impression (in relief) of the object to which the animal is attached.

Order **Veneroida**
Superfamily Lucinacea: 15 British species in 3 families.

A group of bivalves with colourless dull shells, typically circular in outline, that are often very difficult to identify. The anterior adductor scar is sometimes larger than the posterior. Filter feeders with short siphons, these are shallow burrowers in offshore sands and gravels.

Superfamily Galeommatacea: 12 British marine species, in 5 families.

Coin shells form a group of small, globular, bivalves often living in association with a larger invertebrate (often an echinoderm, but sometimes a crustacean or a worm) – although *Lasaea adansoni* (= *L. rubra*) inhabits tufts of the lichen *Lichina pygmaea* on the middle shore. Some species attach themselves to their substratum with a byssus. All are simultaneous hermaphrodites.

Superfamily Cyamiacea: 4 British species in a single family.

Very small (barely 1.5mm across), fragile equivalve inhabitants of fine substrata from the low intertidal to about 30m.

Superfamily Astartacea: 7 British species, in a single family.

A small group, with rather solid, well-formed shells; generally with a prominent concentric sculpture. The two adductor muscles are of approximately equal size. Filter feeders with short siphons, these are shallow burrowers in offshore sands and gravels.

Superfamily Cardiacea: 13 British species in a single family.

Cockles live in the surface layers of sandy substrata, filter feeding through short siphons. Identification depends on the number, and ornamentation, of the numerous radiating ribs on the globular shell.

Superfamily Mactracea: 10 British marine species in a single family.

Trough shells and otter shells form a group of deep burrowers with rather solid and well-formed shells. All have a prominent triangular internal ligament pit called a chondrophore.

Superfamily Solenacea: 7 British species, in 2 families.

Razor shells are so named because they resemble the shape of a cut-throat razor. Very rapid burrowers, they live near the surface, upright in the sand, betraying their presence by a key-hole shaped depression.

Superfamily Tellinacea: 32 British species, in 4 families.

Tellins have thin, flattened and often very colourful shells, which always have hinge teeth and a deep pallial sinus. Deep burrowers, they have long siphons which grope across the surface for the detritus upon which they feed.

Superfamily Arcticacea: 2 British species in separate families.

Arctica islandica is a large (12cm across) globular shell, that lives on firm sandy bottoms from low water mark downwards. A short siphoned filter feeder.

Superfamily Glossacea: 1 British species.

The heart cockle, *Glossus humanus*, is a globular filter feeder with short siphons, chiefly notable for the shell's enrolled umbones. Sublittoral, below 7m., on sedimentary substrata.

Superfamily Veneracea: 19 British species in 2 families.

The shells of venus clams and carpet-shells are mostly solid, with two muscle scars, prominent hinge teeth and, typically, with a pallial sinus, indicating a deep burrowing habit. Some, though, live in rock crevices and one, *Petricola pholadiformis*, is a true borer.

Order **Myoida**:

Superfamily Myacea: 5 British species, in 2 families.

Most gapers and basket shells burrow in soft sediments, with long siphons up to the surface, but *Sphenia binghami* lives in rock crevices or *Laminaria* holdfasts, attached by its byssus.

Superfamily Gastrochaenacea: 1 British species.

Gastrochaena dubia, the flask shell, gets its name from the shape of the excavation it makes whilst boring into sedimentary rocks.

Superfamily Hiatellacea: 4 British species, in a single family.

Hiatella arctica, the rock borer, nestles in crevices of one kind or another; but the other species burrow in offshore sand and mud. The pallial line is often interrupted.

Superfamily Pholadacea: 18 British species in 2 families.

These are the great borers: piddocks burrow into peat, wood, and mudstone, and shipworms burrow into wood. Piddocks gain no nutriment from the rock, into which they burrow, but shipworms are able to digest something from the wood they bore.

Order **Pholadomyoida**

Superfamily Thraciacea: 6 species in 2 families.

These are small (less than 40mm), bivalves of sandy or muddy-sandy substrata from the intertidal zone down to about 60m.

Superfamily Pandoracea: 3 British species in 2 families.

Lantern shells and Pandora's boxes have fragile brittle shells that are never attractively coloured or ornamented. One valve is typically larger than the other, and often is of a different shape. The adductor muscle scars are roughly equal in side and connected by a discontinuous pallial line formed by a series of small scars. Generally found in muddy sand from the lower shore down to approximately 60m.

Super-Order **Septibranchia**
Order **Poromyoida**

These are the only true carnivore within the group, using the gill as a muscular pump to draw food (mostly dead crustacea) into the mantle cavity. The animals live at depth and have dull, brittle shells.

Superfamily Poromyacea: 1 British species.

Poromya granulata has an almost equilateral shell (about 13mm long) and has been found at about 70m off the west coast of Scotland.

Superfamily Cuspidariacea: 7 British species in a single family.

All in the genus *Cuspidaria* – a genus characterised by the posterior part of the shell being drawn out into a projecting spout. Up to 25mm in length, but mostly smaller than 10mm. Found from 18m and deeper, typically in muddy substrata.

Class **Cephalopoda**

Squids, Cuttlefishes and Octopods are clearly the most advanced group of molluscs. The shell is reduced, internal or absent. The head has large, complex, eyes complete with cornea and lens. The mantle is a large muscular cavity, opening beneath the head via a funnel (formed by the foot) through which water can be squirted to provide jet propulsion. Sexes are separate and fertilisation is internal following copulation; some of the male's tentacles being modified for the purpose. Marine. See Muus (1963).

Order **Sepioida**: 18 British species in 3 families.

Cuttlefishes have eight short arms and two long tentacles, retractable into pits. Tentacles bearing suckers only on the spooned tips. A long fin fringes each side of the body, not quite meeting at the rear (Sepiidae) or there are shorter ear-shaped fins about half way along each flank (Sepiolidae). The internal shell of a true cuttle (Sepiidae) is an oval calcified body, lighter than water 'cuttlebone'. In little cuttles (Sepiolidae) the internal shell is chitinous and rudimentary. *Spirula* (Spirulidae) has a coiled tubular internal shell.

Order **Teuthoida**: 21 British species in 9 families.

Squids have ten tentacles, two of which may be longer than the others, not retractable into pits, and bearing suckers only on the spooned tips. Lateral fins meet at the rear end of the body, which may be extended to a long 'tail'. The internal shell is reduced to a horny pen.

Order **Octopoda**: 6 British species in 2 families.

Octopods have eight sessile arms but no tentacles. A pair of fins, not meeting around the rear of the body, are present on the sides of pelagic species in the sub-Order Cirromorpha, but they are absent in the benthic sub-Order Incirrata (*Octopus* and *Eledone*).

? Phylum LOPHOPHORATA

Several authors, including Emig (1979), regard the groups of Phorona, Bryozoa and Brachiopoda as Classes within the Phylum Lophophorata. Pearse *et al.* (1987) devote their Chapter 26 to lophophorates and use the term for a general grouping of three related phyla. That is the view followed here.

Phylum PHORONA

Peanut worms are a small, exclusively marine, group of lophophorate animals which secrete, and then live freely within, cylindrical chitinous tubes. The tubes may be found singly or in clusters, buried in or encrusting rocks and shells, or embedded in mud sand or gravel. The digestive tract is 'U' shaped within the body, so that the anus is close, but peripheral to, the mouth on the oral disc. Some 10 species are currently recognised, world-wide, in 2 genera. The three species known to occur in Britain, and two others which are probably present, all belong to the genus *Phoronis*. See Emig (1979).

Phylum BRACHIOPODA

Lamp shells are bilaterally-symmetrical, unsomited, sedentary marine animals enclosed within a bivalved shell and either cemented to the substratum or attached thereto by a flexible stalk or pedicle. The valves are dorsal and ventral to the body, and not lateral as in bivalve molluscs. Most of the space within the valves is occupied by a large (circular, spiral or complex-looped) system of hollow tentacles called a lophophore. The body itself is small and is located posteriorly. The sexes are typically separate and fertilisation is external, the eggs hatching into a planktonic larva.

  Brachiopods are an ancient group, with over 12,000 of the described species extinct. The modern fauna is restricted to some 350 species, of which 21 are considered British. See Howard, Brunton & Curry (1979): Hayward & Ryland (1990; 1995).

  Howard, Brunton & Curry (1979) do not regard these animals as a Class of the Phylum Lophophorata.

Class Inarticulata
   The shell valves, normally composed of calcium phosphate and chitin, are held together by muscles. The lophophore is not supported by a skeletal framework. The gut has an anus as well as a mouth.

   Order **Acrotretida**: 2 British species in separate families.
   Small animals (> 15mm across), circular in outline, with the lower valve cemented to a hard substratum. Look rather like a limpet (as the lower valve is not visible in life) but have very long radiating setae around the margin, and no shell ribs.

Class Articulata

Shell valves composed of calcium carbonate, and articulated by means of hinge teeth and sockets. The lophophore typically has a supporting skeleton. The blind gut lacks an anus. The animals are attached to the substratum by a stalk (pedicle).

Order **Rhynchonellida**: 3 British species in separate families.
The lophophore has two spirally-coiled lobes, supported by spikes. The solid shell is not perforated by canals.

Order **Terebratulida**: 16 British species in 6 families.
The lophophore is formed of two simple lateral loops and a coiled central lobe supported by a loop. The shell valves are penetrated by canals.

Phylum BRYOZOA

Moss animals. These are sedentary, colonial, aquatic animals whose colonies form a conspicuous part of the epifauna in many marine habitats. Each colony comprises from a few to millions of zooids, formed by asexual division from an original founding ancestrula. Each zooid is in tissue contact with its neighbours. Each is an unsomited, bilaterally-symmetrical, polyp with a circular or crescentic series of slender tentacles (the lophophore), a body (metasome) and, in some cases, a small preoral episome. The epidermis of each zooid secretes a gelatinous, horny or calcareous shell which encloses the colony, except for the apertures through which the lophophores are extended (and retracted) by muscles. These apertures are sometimes protected by opercula. Typically, each zooid has a U-shaped gut with a mouth within, and an anus outside, the lophophore. Each zooid is small (about 0.5mm) but the colonies may be large. They vary in shape from flat encrustations and foliose arboraceous structures to widely separated zooids connected by stolons. Within a colony, zooids may be polymorphic with particular individuals specialised for feeding (autozooids), or for various other functions (heterozooids) e.g., defence, or brooding the young. Colonies are hermaphrodite, although individual polyps may be hermaphrodite or single sexed. Some families have planktonic larvae. Members of one Class, the Phylactolaemata, live in fresh water, all the others are marine. World-wide, the number of living species substantially exceeds 4,000.

Class Stenolaemata

The zooids are cylindrical and the body wall is calcified. The lophophore is everted by a mechanism based on the redistribution of internal coelomic pressures. Colonies show limited polymorphism. There are four Orders, but only one of them contains living species.

Order **Cyclostomatida**: 36 British marine species, in 9 families.
Zooid apertures are circular, terminal, and without any specialised closing apparatus. Embryos are brooded in conspicuous gonozooids. See Hayward & Ryland (1985; 1990; 1995).

Class Gymnolaemata

The zooids are cylindrical or squat and the body wall may or may not be calcified. The lophophore is everted by distortion of the body wall. Colonies show polymorphism.

Order **Ctenostomatida**: 45 British marine species, in 17 families.
The zooids are cylindrical, flask-shaped or flattened. Encrusting, erect or creeping. The orifice is (primitively) terminal, closed by muscular contraction, and appears to be puckered or squared. The uncalcified body wall is membranous or gelatinous. Embryos are typically brooded within the parent zooid. See Hayward (1985): Hayward & Ryland (1990; 1995).

Order **Cheilostomatida**: 219 species in 40 families.
The zooids calcified and typically box-shaped. Orifice frontal or sub-terminal, closed by a hinged flap (the operculum). Embryos are typically brooded in ovicells or ovisacs. The old division of the Order into Anasca and Ascophora has been abandoned. See Hayward & Ryland (1990; 1995; 1997; and in preparation).

Phylum ENTOPROCTA

This is a clearly-defined group of small, sessile, filter-feeding animals. They are unsomited and bilaterally-symmetrical with a rounded body (calyx) bearing, aborally, a cylindrical attachment stalk and, orally, a horseshoe-shaped ring of between 8 and 36 tentacles – which can contract and fold inwards. All entoprocts are suspension feeders, either living commensally with a larger animal or free-living and colonial. As in the Bryozoa, the gut is U-shaped but, in entoprocts, both mouth and anus are located within the tentacular ring. Members of this phylum will rarely be found by accident (except in the lab). Solitary species must be searched for on or about their hosts, whilst colonial forms may be seen as a whitish fuzz on other encrusting organisms, low on the shore. See Nielson (1989): Hayward & Ryland (1990; 1995).

Order **Solitaria**: at least 15 British marine species, in a single family.
Solitary entoprocts, family Loxosomatidae, are all marine and are typically found (gregariously) associated with larger invertebrates – either attached to their host or living in its burrow or tube – which produce water currents for respiration and feeding. Individuals are small (<0.5mm in height). Daughter individuals are budded off from the oral wall of the calyx. Sometimes found free-living in aquarium systems or on panels used for fouling studies.

Order **Coloniales**: 7 British marine species, in 2 families.
The colonial entoprocts are common members of the fouling communities of stones, algae, shells, crabs and man-made objects in shallow seas. Some species also occur in brackish waters but only one, *Urnatella gracilis*, is found in freshwater (although not yet in Britain). Individual zooids, about 2mm in height, typically arise from a stolon, creeping over the substratum.

Phylum CYCLIOPHORA

A phylum established by Funch & Kristensen (1995) for their 'new' species, *Symbion pandora*, described from the mouthparts of a Norway lobster (*Nephrops norvegicus*) collected in the Kattegat. Whilst specimens have been found on *N. norvegicus* from Sweden and from Faroe, I am not aware of any British records but the host is widespread.

Order **Simbiida**: only one species described to date.

S. pandora is an acoelomate bilaterally-symmetrical marine metazoan, 347 μm long by 113 μm wide. Sessile solitary asexual feeding stages (so far, found only on the mouthparts of *N. norvegicus*) produce free-swimming motile stages of three types: (a) an asexual brooding larva (Pandora larva) which settles on the same host, containing new feeding stages, or (b) a dwarf male which settles on a feeding stage, or (c) a female, which also settles on the same host. Females eventually degenerate and give rise to dispersive Chordoid larvae which colonise a fresh host. All motile stages are short lived and do not feed. Presumably the life cycle is correlated with the moult cycle of the host. See Funch & Kristensen (1995).

Phylum ARTHROPODA

The animals with jointed legs represent the most successful group of invertebrates. Insects dominate the land and crustaceans the seas. They are bilaterally-symmetrical, metamerically-somited animals with a jointed exoskeleton which is moulted periodically to permit growth. Although traditionally regarded as a co-herent group, extensive work by embryologists (including Anderson, 1973; Manton, 1979; Tiegs & Manton, 1958) cast doubt on their presumed mono-phyletic origin. They could find no convincing evidence for linking the major arthropod taxa – trilobites, crustaceans, insects and arachnids – and concluded that they must have arisen independently from non-arthropod ancestors. Their view gathered adherents and the concept of treating Crustacea, Chelicerata and Uniramia (= myriapods and insects) as separate phyla was becoming accepted in the 1980s (e.g., Barnes, 1984). Recently, Shear (1992) quoting Kukalová-Peck's (1992) work on Lower Permian fossil insects from the Urals, rejects 'Uniramia' as a taxon on the grounds that it was based on a falsehood. The uniramian and biramian leg patterns of living arthropods are shown to be derived from a polyramous ancestral leg. Shear concludes that there is no longer any reason for doubting the reality of Arthropoda as a phylum.

Sub-Phylum CRUSTACEA

With approximately 39,000 living species, the crustaceans include the animals popularly known as barnacles, crabs, lobsters, shrimps, woodlice and water fleas – as well as many other lesser known groups. They are bilaterally-symmetrical, metamerically somited[20] animals with biramous limbs and a jointed exoskeleton that is moulted periodically to permit growth.

---

[20] Somite or segment? There is confusion of terminology in the literature. Some authors use the word 'segment' for the body of, for example, a worm or a shrimp. Others use it for the sections of arthropod appendages. I have tried to follow the latter convention and use 'somite' for the replicated sections of the body.

The body comprises a presomital acron, a post-somital telson and an intervening series of somites organised into three tagmata: head (5 somites), thorax (8 somites) and abdomen (6 or 7 somites). The head bears five pairs of appendages: antennules (1st antennae), antennae (2nd antennae), mandibles (jaws), and two pairs of accessory jaws (1st and 2nd maxillae). Each thoracic and abdominal somite originally bore one pair of appendages, but those on the abdomen have become variously reduced or lost. Each appendage consists of a basal protopodite from which arise an inner, endopodite, and an outer, exopodite, both multiarticulate. Each of the three basal limb sections may bear projections, termed respectively epipodites, endites and exites, some of which may function as gills.

In many species, a fold of exoskeleton (the carapace) extends dorsally and laterally back from the head to cover some or all of the anterior somites. The sexes are typically separate, and fertilisation is typically by copulation. The eggs are often brooded and typically hatch into a larval stage.

About 1,200 species may be considered British.

Crustacean Larval Forms

Some crustaceans lay large numbers of small eggs, each with a small supply of yolk. Others lay many fewer, large yolky eggs. One general rule is that the smaller the supply of yolk, the earlier is the stage at which the larva hatches. The other is that the head region develops first and posterior somites are developed later so that the youngest larvae have fewest legs, and the oldest the most.

Examples can be found, in every Class of the Crustacea, in which the egg hatches into a nauplius larva, with three pairs of appendages (antennules, antennae and mandibles). There is a medial simple eye, a large labrum and a pair of frontal organs in the form of papillae or filaments. The commonest nauplii in coastal plankton hauls are those of copepods and acorn barnacles.

There follows a succession of larval stages in which more and more somites and limbs are added, although not necessarily in the adult order from front to rear. Changes in form occur at each moult. In branchiopods, the adult form is reached gradually, by the addition of a few somites at a time from a growth zone just in front of the telson. In gradual development of this kind, the successive instars are not sufficiently different to warrant stadial names. More commonly, however, growth is metamorphic and more abrupt changes occur at some moults.

In a zoea larva, the main divisions of the body are obvious and the animal swims, mainly, by means of its biramous maxillipeds. Other thoracic legs are added, posteriorly, in later zoeal stages. In those crustacea which have the final megalopa stage, the adult body form is previewed, although even those of crabs swim by using the abdominal appendages.

Rather confusingly, particular names have been given to these latter stages in some groups of Crustacea. These names are historical accidents, being the generic names assigned to the larvae before their link with the adult form had been established.

Class Branchiopoda

Very small planktonic crustaceans, mostly found in freshwater, with a short body, a reduced, unsegmented, antennule and leaf-like thoracic limbs with epipodal gills. The abdomen is without appendages except for the caudal furca. A characteristic meta-nauplius larva has numerous somites and adds extra appendages at each moult. The carapace, when present, forms a bivalve shell. Compound eyes are typically present. Females are frequently parthenogenetic.

Order **Cladocera**: 6 British marine species in 2 genera.

Most water fleas are freshwater animals, but there are a few marine species. They are small planktonic crustacea, up to 1mm in length, with a distinctive carapace. It is all of one piece, but folded along its longitudinal axis to form a pseudo-bivalve shell, enclosing the body but not the head. There is a prominent, median, sessile, compound eye. The thorax bears four pairs of legs. The posterior end of the abdomen is flexed forwards, with a prominent claw-like furca. Males are smaller than females.

Class **Tantulocarida** at least 1 British species.

Minute (ca 0.1mm long) ectoparasites of other crustaceans, mostly tanaids, copepods, cumaceans or isopods. Like some cladocerans, there is a double-loop life cycle in which the sexual phase appears to be extremely short-lived. The non-feeding, free-swimming (or hyper-benthic and undiscovered) males and females are presumed to practice internal fertilisation. The eggs hatch directly as tantulus larvae (which must be exceptional amongst crustaceans in lacking any head appendages). The tantulus attaches itself firmly to a host and proceeds to grow, without any sign of the usual crustacean moulting process, into a parthenogenetic female which remains attached to the host through the larval oral disc. This female, also, releases tantulus larvae. It is not known whether there is a simple alteration between the sexual and parthenogenetic multiplication phases, or whether some genetic switch mechanism is involved. See Boxshall & Lincoln (1987) and Huys, Boxshall & Lincoln (1993).

Class **Cirripedia**

Free-living or parasitic, adult barnacles are sessile, after a free-swimming larval phase. Parasitic forms are generally highly modified and only recognisable as barnacles by their nauplius larvae. Free-living forms are attached to their chosen substratum by a cement secreted from the antennules. The adult's appendages comprise mandibles, first and second maxillae, and the cirri. The first and second cirri are typically short, functioning as maxillipeds, whilst pairs 3-6 are used to comb food particles from the water. Most species are hermaphrodite with cross-fertilisation via an elongate penis. All are marine. See Anderson (1994) for a general review: but Southward & Crisp (1963); Bassindale (1960); Hayward & Ryland (1990, 1995) for British species. The group is sometimes regarded as a subclass, within the Class Thecostraca, e.g. by Anderson (1994) or the Class Maxillopoda, e.g. by Pearse *et al.* (1987).

Order **Thoracica**

Sub-Order Pedunculata: 9 British species in 2 families.

Scalpellum scalpellum is our only resident stalked barnacle, living in the shallow sub-littoral, although there are perhaps 3 others in deeper water offshore. These animals mainly drift to these latitudes on their float (*Dosima fascicularis*) or attached to floating driftwood (typically *Lepas anatifera*), or other objects – *Conchoderma* sp. are found on whales. Two parasitic species, *Alepas parasitica* living on the jellyfish *Cyanea* and *Anelasma squalicola*, on the very rare shark *Etmopterus spinax*, have also been recorded. For larval forms, see Moyse (1987).

Sub-Order Sessilia

Tribe Verrucomorpha: 1 British species.

Verruca stroemia is an asymmetrical acorn barnacle, found from the lower shore down to a depth of 500m all around the British Isles.

Tribe Balanomorpha;: 12 British species in 4 families.

Typical acorn barnacles are very abundant on rocky sea shores, and other places provided with currents of moving surface water. Their conical shells have a perimeter wall comprising four or six plates, some or all of which may be fused together, with four moveable opercular plates closing the central aperture. Most species are free-living, but two are associated with sponges (*Acasta spongites* is always embedded in *Dysidea fragilis*) and *Megatrema anglicum* is always associated with the solitary coral *Caryophyllia smithi*. *Coronula diadema* lives on the skin of humpback whales and *Xenobalanus globicipitis* on the porpoise. For further information about *Acasta* and its relatives see Kolbasov (1993). For larval forms, see Lang (1980).

Order **Acrothoracica**: 1 British species.

Burrowing barnacles form a small Order of some 40 known species, in 3 families, all of which occupy calcareous substrata – such as the shell of a mollusc inhabited by a hermit crab. This Order comprises the family Trypetesidae. *Trypetesa lampas* lives in a cavity excavated in the columella of a whelk, usually *Buccinum undatum*, shell occupied by the hermit crab *Pagurus bernhardus*. The cirri are so short that they cannot be extended outside the burrow, and the animal probably feeds on the hermit's waste food or faeces. The opening to the burrow is visible from the outside as a very small slit, typically the size and shape of a typed comma. Dwarf males live parasitically in the mantle of the females. See Tomlinson (1987).

Order **Rhizocephala**

Endoparasites of other crustacea. The female body is a fleshy tumour nourished by a root-like system of absorptive roots which permeate the host's body and invade all tissues except the heart, gills and nervous system. Dwarf males are parasitic in the mantle cavity of the female. See Høeg (1995) for a general review of the Order. Controversy surrounds the relationship between the Rhizocephala and other cirripede Orders. Traditionally, they have been regarded as barnacles on account of their larval stages but Newman (1987) cites their sexually dimorphic eggs and nauplii (cf. the hermaphroditism of the other Orders) as a reason to consider them a sister group to the Cirripedia within the Class, or sub-phylum, Maxillopoda. Pearse *et al.* (1987) follows this line but Moyse, (in Hayward & Ryland, 1990, 1995), Anderson (1994) and Høeg (1995) do not.

Separation into Sub-Orders depends on the developmental life-history, so identification in the field depends upon recognising the host.

Sub-Order Kentrogonida: 19 British species in 3 families.

Endoparasites of Decapod crustacea. Members of the Sacculinidae parasitise true crabs (Brachyura). Members of the other families attack Anomura: Lernaeodiscidae on squat lobsters (Galatheidae) and burrowing prawns (Thalassinidea); Peltogastridae are found on various hermit crabs (Paguridae) but not on *Pagurus bernhardus* (Hayward & Ryland, 1995).

Sub-Order Akentrogonida: 4 'British' species in 3 families.

Members of the family Chthamalophilidae are parasites of balanomorph barnacles. The two species involved, *Chthamalophilus delagei* and *Boschmaella balani*, have been recorded in NW France and may be expected to appear in SW England. *Sylon hippolytes* (Sylonidae) attacks various shrimps and prawns whilst *Clistosaccus paguri* (Clistosaccidae) is found on hermit crabs, including *P. bernhardus* (Hayward & Ryland, 1995).

Class Ostracoda

Seed shrimps are small, often benthic, crustaceans, totally enclosed within a bivalved carapace, which is shed and reconstituted at each moult. The body is not somited, externally, but carries 5-7 pairs of appendages. The Class is divided into 6 Orders, 3 of which have living representatives.

Order **Myodocopida**: 86 British species in 4 families.
A wholly marine Order. Many truly pelagic members live in the open sea whilst others are benthonic swimmers in the shallow sub-littoral. The carapace is often relatively large, up to 30mm long, with (or without) an anterior rostral incisure but always with a convex ventral margin. The outer lamella is typically weakly calcified, thin and flexible. It is typically weakly ornamented and smooth. There are between five and seven pairs of appendages. The abdominal furca is triangular, lamelliform and armed with strong marginal chelate setae. See Angel (1993).

Order **Platycopida**
A marine Order, with a few brackish-water species, mostly benthonic in fairly deep waters. The carapace is typically less than 1mm long, without an anterior rostral incisure, and ovate in outline. The valves are unequal so that the right overlaps the left around the entire margin. There are seven pairs of appendages. The abdominal furca is lamelliform with strong chelate setae.

Order **Podocopida**: 116 British marine species, in 19 families.
An Order of marine, brackish, freshwater ostracods with a few terrestrial species. Most are benthonic, littoral or sub-littoral, although some (e.g. in freshwater) are nektonic. The carapace may be up to 8mm long, but is typically less than 1mm, and is without an anterior rostral incisure. The valves are typically strongly calcified, but may be ornamented or smooth. There may be six or seven pairs of appendages. The abdominal furca is narrow, lamelliform and bearing a few setae – or is reduced or is absent. See Athersuch, Horne & Whittaker (1989).

Class Copepoda

Copepods, forming the second largest Class of the Crustacea (after Malacostraca), are typically small (less than 0.5mm) animals. The short, often rounded, body is composed of a head (fused to the first thoracic somite) followed by 8 free somites and the telson – with further fusion in some families. There is no carapace and there are no paired eyes, but free-living species have a well-developed median eye. Antennules are uniramous. The appendages of the first thoracic somite are modified as maxillipeds, followed by four or five pairs of 'normal' thoracic appendages. The abdomen is narrow, without appendages, and ends in a caudal furca. Commensal, free-living and parasitic species inhabit terrestrial, freshwater and marine habitats. Parasitic species are highly modified, and most easily identified from determination of their host's identity. The Class is divided into 8 Orders. See Huys & Boxshall (1991) and Huys, Gee, Moore & Hamond (1996) for harpacticoids; Kabata (1993) and Gotto (1993) for parasitic forms. Pearse *et al.* (1987) treats Copepoda as a sub-class of the Order Maxillopoda.

Order **Platycopioida**: 1 (possibly 2) British species in the genus *Platycopia*.
Platycopioids are small (1mm), free-living copepods that inhabit the hyperbenthic community in relatively shallow seas. Antennules short. Body with an articulation between the thorax and the abdomen. Eyes absent. See Huys & Boxshall (1991).

126   J. H. CROTHERS

Order **Calanoida**: at least 24 British marine species.

Free-living. calanoids are the marine planktonic copepods *par excellence*. The long antennules are used for swimming. Antennae biramous. Body with an articulation between thorax and abdomen. Many are facultative small particle feeders consuming phytoplankton, others are predators of zooplankton. All appear to be capable of catching food particles raptorially. Marine and freshwater. See Huys & Boxshall (1991).

Order **Misophrioida**: 1 British species, *Misophrya pallida*.

Twenty species of free-living copepods, misophrioids occur in shallow coastal waters as well as in deep water below 2,000m. They are opportunistic gorgers, feeding on a variety of other copepods and coelenterates. The antennules are short and prehensile; antennae biramous. The body has an articulation between the 4th and 5th free thoracic somites (lost in some parasitic forms). Female carries one egg sac. Marine. See Huys & Boxshall (1991).

Order **Cyclopoida**: 57 British species (in 2 families) live in association with other marine invertebrates: at least 10 others are free-living.

Free-living and parasitic. Cyclopoids are by far the most abundant and successful groups of copepods in freshwater, particularly the planktonic family Cyclopidae. The other free-living families are mainly marine – benthic Cyclopinidae and planktonic Oithonidae. The marine parasitic forms typically attack ascidians but some species prefer soft corals or brittle stars. Antennules short; antennae uniramous. Body with an articulation between the 4th and 5th free thoracic somites (lost in some parasitic forms). Female carries 2 egg sacs, Marine and freshwater, planktonic and benthic. See Gotto (1993) for the species living in association with other invertebrates.

Order **Mormonilloida**: 2 species in the genus *Mormonilla*.

Two species of free-living planktonic copepods, widespread in the world's oceans between 400 and 1,500m depth. The elongate antennules have three or four long segments; antennae biramous. The body has an articulation between the 4th and 5th free thoracic somites Without a heart and without 5th or 6th pairs of legs. See Huys & Boxshall (1991).

Order **Harpacticoida**: around 800 British marine and brackish-water species.

A large Order of, mostly, free-living primarily benthic copepods, with a small body, tapering posteriorly and, typically, without any marked constriction. Antennules very short; antennae biramous. Body with an articulation between the 4th and 5th free thoracic somites. Benthic and planktonic, freshwater and, mostly, marine. They are usually the second most abundant group (after nematodes) in marine sediments reaching densities in excess of 1,000 10cm^{-2}! Infaunal species can be categorised as interstitial, burrowing or epibenthic forms. Interstitial species are small, with elongate worm-like bodies. About 800 species, belonging to over 190 genera, are known between Brest and Bergen but there are doubtless many more yet to be described. See Huys, Gee, Moore & Hamond (1996). Twenty-two British species live in association with other invertebrates. See Gotto (1993).

Order **Poecilostomatoida**: 107 species in 20 families are associated with fish or other marine invertebrates.

Ectoparasitic or otherwise associated with other animals: decapod crustacea, coelenterates, fish, molluscs and polychaetes. Twenty-one species (in five families) are parasitic on British fishes; eighty-six species (in fifteen families) are associated with invertebrates. Members of four families are planktonic. Antennules often well-developed; antennae uniramous. Body with an articulation between the 4th and 5th free thoracic somites (lost in some parasitic forms). Largely marine, but there is a small number of fish parasites in freshwater. See Kabata (1979; 1993) for the species parasitic on fish and Gotto (1993) for the species living in association with other invertebrates.

Order **Siphonostomatoida**: 161 British marine species in 24 families.

A large Order (in excess of 1,550 species) all of which are ectoparasitic or otherwise associated with other animals: 66% with fish (or mammals) and the others with the lobster, nudibranchs, bivalves, or echinoderms. 75% of copepods parasitic on fishes belong to this Order. Ninety-five species (in fourteen families) are parasitic on British marine fish (3 more are parasitic on our freshwater fish). Sixty-six species live in association with other marine invertebrates Antennules reduced and prehensile uniramous antennae. Body with an articulation between the 3rd and 4th or 4th and 5th free thoracic somites (lost in some parasitic forms). See Kabata (1979; 1993) for the species parasitic on fish and Gotto (1993) for the species living in association with other invertebrates (and whales).

Order **Monstrilloida**: about 26 British species, in 1 family.

The larvae parasitise tubicolous polychaetes (*Thaumaleus*) or gastropods (*Monstrilla*). The nauplius stage is infective. Adults are free-living but they do not feed, being without antennae, mouthparts or gut, although they typically have well-developed antennules. Females carry their eggs on long ovigerous spines. Marine. See Isaac (1974; 1975).

Class Malacostraca

Small to very large crustaceans, mostly marine, and often with a heavily calcified exoskeleton. They typically have stalked compound eyes, eight thoracic somites and six (rarely seven) abdominal somites. A carapace is typically present, covering head and thorax but never more than the first or second abdominal somite. The appendages of the first three thoracic somites may form additional mouthparts, the maxillipeds, typically leaving 5 pairs of walking legs (pereiopods). The abdominal appendages are often modified for swimming (pleopods) or reproduction; the last pair (uropods) are typically broad and, with the telson, form a tail fan. Pearse *et al.* (1987) offer an alternative classification. The Phyllocarida and Hoplocarida are raised to Sub-classes whilst the Peracarida and Eucarida are grouped, with two other super-orders that lack British representatives, into the sub-class Eumalacostraca.

Super-Order: Phyllocarida

Order **Leptostraca**: 7 British species.

A very small Order comprising about a dozen extant species (but see below): probably the most primitive of all the Malacostraca. The large bilobed carapace is formed by fusion of the dorsal parts of the head and those of all the thoracic somites, extending backwards to cover at least the first 4 abdominal somites. None of the eight pairs of thoracic legs is chelate, or modified as maxillipeds. An anterior extension of the carapace, the hinged rostral plate, covers the head. They are thought to be omnivorous deposit feeders. There is no larval stage, eggs being brooded within the carapace to emerge as 'miniature adults'. All are marine.

Traditionally, taxonomists have regarded this Order as comprising a few nearly cosmopolitan species. This concept has now been challenged and discrete species recognised from the various faunal regions. See Mauchline (1984) or Dahl (1985) (but not both) each has 4 species of *Nebalia* but they are not reconcilable. For Mauchline, the common British species is *N. bipes* whilst Dahl maintains this species to live farther north and the common temperate form to be *N. herbstii*.

Super-Order Holpocarida
Order **Stomatopoda**: 2 British species.

Mantis shrimps form a small discrete Order of crustaceans. There are about 200 species, world wide, mostly in warmer water. The few caught in Britain represent the most northerly records of these animals. The carapace is formed by fusion of the dorsal parts of the head and those of the first 4 thoracic somites, leaving somites 5-8 free. The first five pairs of thoracic legs are sub-chelate maxillipeds: the second pair being enormously developed and reminiscent of the preying mantis (insect). This leaves three pairs of legs for walking. The forward end of the carapace projects forwards between the, large, stalked, eyes as a short rostrum. Mantis shrimps are thought to be carnivores of shrimps and worms. Both British species may exceed 70mm in length. The sexes are separate. Larvae are much more often recorded than adults; individuals pass through 9 stages on their way to adulthood Both British species are marine, probably living in burrows in the shallow sub-littoral. See Mauchline (1984).

Super-Order Peracarida

Orders in which a single thoracic somite is fused with the head; in which the female incubates the young in a brood pouch (marsupium) formed by epipodites (oostegites) of some thoracic limbs; and in which there is no free-living larval stage.

Order **Mysidacea**: 74 British species, in 8 families.

Opossum shrimps are small, free-swimming crustaceans in which the carapace is formed by fusion of the dorsal parts of the head and those of the first three thoracic somites, extending back over most of the others; but allowing at least part of the last thoracic somite to be seen on the back. The thoracic appendages form one or two pairs of maxillipeds; followed by six or seven pairs of similar pereiopods. These are of a distinctive form, in which the endopod can be used for walking or holding prey, whilst the exopod, which rises up around the edges of the carapace, is used for swimming. The forward end of the carapace extends as a small rostrum between the large compound eyes, which are on, sometimes prominent, moveable eyestalks. Most species are colourless, even transparent, and have a conspicuous, circular, statocyst at the base of each endopod. The swimming legs produce a water current that carries fine suspended matter to the mid-ventral line. Most mysids filter the edible component from this current with their maxillipeds but they may also seize copepods and other similar sized objects in their 'walking' legs. Body length ranges between 10 and 25mm. The sexes are separate. The young emerge from the marsupium as 'miniature adults' lacking the secondary sexual characteristics which appear later. With the exception of *Mysis relicta*, all British species are marine or estuarine. See Tattersall & Tattersall (1951); Makings (1977).

Order **Cumacea**: 41 British species, in 7 families.

In cumaceans, the carapace is formed by fusion of the dorsal parts of the head and those of the first three thoracic somites – leaving the remaining 5 free. The first three thoracic appendages form maxillipeds, and the other five bear pairs of thoracic legs, none of which is chelate. The forward end of the carapace extends over the antennae as a pseudorostrum. Eyes sessile. Head and thorax much larger than the narrow abdomen, giving the animal something of a 'tadpole-like' appearance. Most cumaceans feed on micro-organisms and the organic content of mud but some genera may take foraminiferids and even small crustaceans. *Diastylis rathkei* may reach 22mm in length but all the other British species are between 2 and 14mm, mostly around 6mm. The sexes are separate. The young emerge from the marsupium at a stage closely resembling the adult, but lacking the last pair of thoracic legs (pereiopods). Fertilisation to emergence takes between 1 and 3 months depending on species and water temperature. Longevity is between 6 and 18 months. All British species are marine, scarcely entering estuaries. See Jones (1976).

Order **Tanaidacea**: 27 British species, in 8 families.

In tanaids, the carapace is formed by fusion of the dorsal parts of the head and those of the first two thoracic somites – leaving the remaining 6 free. Appendages on the first thoracic somite form the single pair of maxillipeds, those of the second, a pair of chelipeds (bearing chelae), leaving six pairs of walking legs (pereiopods) on the free somites. The forward end of the carapace extends over the antennae as a pseudorostrum. Compound eyes are borne on small anteriorly-directed lobes of the cephalothorax. Most tanaids are raptorial feeders, consuming detritus and its associated micro-organisms. Body length ranges between 1 and 25mm, although most British species are less than 6mm long. The sexes are separate, although possibly sequentially hermaphrodite. The young (mancas) are retained in the marsupium until they have gained most of their appendages. With the exception of *Heterotanais oerstedi*, all British species are marine. See Holdich & Jones (1983).

Order **Isopoda**: at least 85 British marine species, in 18 families.

Free-living isopods are typically dorso-ventrally-flattened crustaceans without a carapace. The first thoracic somite is fused with the head, and its appendages form maxillipeds. The other seven pairs (five in the family Gnathiidae) are typically similar in form (hence 'iso pods'), but in the Anthuridae, the first pair are sub-chelate. Many species are thought to be omnivorous deposit feeders, able to macerate large pieces of food. Some, however, appear essentially herbivorous whilst others (e.g. *Eurydice*) are highly predaceous carnivores. For breeding, the sexes first come together at pre-copula when males carry females for a short period until the moult at which copulation takes place. Sperm is transferred in spermatophores. Typically, eggs are released into, and incubated within, a ventral thoracic brood chamber from which the juveniles subsequently emerge as 'miniature adults', although lacking some somites and legs.

Members of the Suborder Epicaridea are all parasitic, invariably associated with another crustacean, often showing extreme specialisation and loss of body form in the adult. Free living species of isopod occur in the marine environment from the littoral to abyssal zones, others are found in estuaries or freshwater, and one suborder, the Oniscoidea (see Hopkin, 1991; Oliver & Meechan, 1993) is mainly terrestrial. See Naylor (1972).

Order **Amphipoda**

Free-living amphipods are, typically, laterally compressed crustacea without a carapace. The first thoracic somite is fused with the head, and its appendages form maxillipeds. Appendages 2-5 (on free thoracic somites 1-4) are oriented posteriorly; appendages 6-8 anteriorly. The first two pairs of pereiopods are typically subchelate (gnathopods). Of the 5,500 known species of amphipod, 85% belong to the Suborder Gammaridea, 9% to the Hyperiidea, 6% to the Caprellidea and a fraction of 1% to the Ingolfiellidea (supposedly primitive species living interstitially in marine bottom sediments or subterranean ground water.

Suborder Gammaridea: 269 British marine and estuarine species, 10 freshwater and 1 terrestrial; in 38 families.

Sand hoppers (an unfortunate name as most do not live in sand and fewer still hop) are generalist, typically benthic, marine amphipods (known in North America as scuds) with a great diversity of habit and habitat. See Lincoln (1979).

Suborder Hyperiidea: 8 British species, in 2 families.

Specialised marine planktonic amphipods, typically having enormous, often strikingly coloured, eyes covering the entire head, and often with a rather spherical shape. Considerable sexual dimorphism – males have elongate, slender antennae whilst, in females, both pairs are very short. Typically associated with jellyfish, *Hyperia galba* is the only common species. See Shih & Dunbar (1963); Dunbar (1963).

Suborder Caprellidea: at least 14 British marine species, in 2 families.

The two families are very different. The Caprellidae (skeleton shrimps) are benthic marine animals living amongst hydroids and algae. The Cyamidae (whale lice) are specialised ectoparasites of various cetaceans (whales and dolphins). There are some 16 species with a cosmopolitan distribution whose occurrence in British waters obviously depends on the movements of their hosts. See Harrison (1943) and Leung (1967) for whale lice.

Super-Order Eucarida

Order **Euphausiacea**: 16 British species, in 2 families.

In the shrimp-like planktonic euphausiids (krill), the carapace is formed by fusion of the dorsal parts of the head and those of all the thoracic somites. None of the eight pairs of thoracic legs is chelate, or modified as maxillipeds. The forward end of the carapace projects forwards between the large, stalked, eyes as a short rostrum. All euphausiids are omnivorous planktivores, both of phyto- and zoo-plankton. *Meganyctiphanes norvegica* may reach some 40mm in length at the age of 2 years. The sexes are separate. After fertilisation, the eggs are either released into the sea or stuck to appendages. They hatch as nauplii and then pass through several calyptopis and furcilia stages on their way to adulthood. All British species are marine, and many of them are typically found in water over 100m deep. See Mauchline (1984).

Order **Decapoda**: 154 British species, in 34 families.

In shrimps, prawns, crabs and lobsters the carapace is formed by fusion of the dorsal parts of the head and those of all the thoracic somites. The first 3 pairs of thoracic legs are modified as maxillipeds, and the next pair is typically chelate. The forward end of the carapace may or may not project forwards between the, stalked, eyes as a rostrum. Most species are carnivorous. The sexes are separate. After fertilisation, the eggs are typically stuck to abdominal appendages. They hatch as zoea larvae and may then pass through a megalopa stage on their way to adulthood. Most British species are marine, with a few estuarine or freshwater forms. See Smaldon, Holthuis & Fransen (1993) for shrimps and prawns; Ingle (1983; 1996), or Crothers & Crothers (1988) for crabs; Ingle (1993) for hermit crabs; Ingle (1991) for larval crabs. Allen (1967); Hayward & Ryland (1990; 1995) have illustrated keys to all British species. Scholtz & Richter (1995) discuss phylogenetic relationships.

Sub-Phylum CHELICERATA

The 63,000 living species of chelicerates include the animals commonly known as spiders, scorpions, and mites. They are small to medium-sized, bilaterally-symmetrical, metamerically somited animals with uniramous limbs and a body divided into two regions: a cephalothorax (prosoma) formed from the presomital acron plus the six anterior trunk somites; and an abdomen (opisthosoma) with up to thirteen somites and the postsomital telson. The chitinous exoskeleton is moulted periodically to permit growth.

The prosoma bears six pairs of appendages: pre-oral chelicerae (often forming chelae), pedipalps (which may be antenna-like, leg-like or chelate) and four pairs of walking legs. Most British species are terrestrial, with only a few to be found in freshwater and marine habitats.

Some authorities (e.g. Pearse, 1987) would include the sea spiders in this sub-phylum as the Class Pycnogonida. Here, I have followed Hayward & Ryland (1990; 1995) and Hayward *et al.* (1996) and treated them as a separate phylum.

Class Arachnida

The prosoma is covered by a carapace. The opisthosoma has 13 somites, plus a telson (often reduced). Almost all are carnivores, consuming a pre-liquefied food using a pumping pharynx. Essentially a terrestrial group – see Tilling (1987) – but 3 of the constituent Orders contain marine or maritime species.

Order **Aranea**: a marine variety of 1 British species, *Pardosa agrestis*.

Spiders are the best known group of arachnids. The opisthosoma is apparently unsomited and joined to the prosoma by a narrow stalk (pedicel). There is a pair of small appendages (spinnerets) at the back end of the opisthosoma. All 600, or so, British species are predators, mainly of insects and other arthropods.

The wolf spider formerly known as *Pardosa purbeckensis*, is a permanent inhabitant of salt marshes and mud flats, able to survive under water at high tide. However, it is regarded by Roberts (1985) as a marinised variety of *P. agrestis*. The water spider lives in freshwater but all the others are terrestrial and are not confined to the coast even if they are occasionally found there. See Jones-Walters (1989) for a family key. Hayward & Ryland (1990; 1995) note 17 British species, from 5 families, that have been recorded amongst tidal debris and provide a key to those families; See Roth & Brown (1976) for a general account.

Order **Pseudoscorpiones**: 1 British marine species, *Neobisium maritimum*.
False scorpions form the fourth largest Order of arachnids. They are all less than four millimetres long, but may be very abundant. All 25 British species are carnivorous and all, except *Neobisium maritimum*, are terrestrial – although Pugh, in Hayward & Ryland (1990), keys out two more that have been found on the strand line. *N. maritimum* reaches 3.2mm in length. It is a predator of collembolans, found in crevices on sheltered rocky shores down to the middle shore. See Legg & Jones (1988).

Order **Acariformes**: At least 62 British marine species.
Mites comprise much the largest Order of arachnids and are, individually, amongst the smallest in size (and the most difficult to identify!). All are less than two millimetres long. There is no separation into prosoma and opisthosoma and, as the whole body is covered by a carapace, they appear unsomited. The group includes terrestrial and aquatic members, free-living and parasitic.
Suborder Mesostigmata: At least 36 British marine species in 16 families.
A large group with many littoral and supralittoral representatives. Most are predatory or scavenging, feeding on other arthropods (or their eggs), nematodes or carrion. Many species are tolerant of occasional submersion in salt water but have a low tolerance of desiccation, so they are most frequently found in rotting vegetation along the strandline. The life cycle has five stages, egg, larva, protonymph, deuteronymph and adult. The larva has but three pairs of legs. See Hayward & Ryland (1990), Pugh & King (1988).
Suborder Prostigmata: At least 74 British marine species in 14 families; the largest (Halacaridae) has 54 species.
A very large group of diverse forms. Most littoral species have a low tolerance of submersion in salt water but a high tolerance of desiccation, so they are usually found in drier drift vegetation. Most are predatory, feeding on other small arthropods (or their eggs), nematodes or carrion. Some are scavengers whilst members of the sub-family Rhombognathinae (in the family Halacaridae) are herbivores. See Hayward & Ryland (1990; 1995), Pugh & King (1988); Green & Macquitty (1987) for halacarids.
Suborder Cryptostigmata: At least 28 British marine species in 13 Superfamilies.
A large group of typically dark-coloured mites with a well-sclerotised or leathery integument. Most are fungus-feeders and, hence, most littoral species are late invaders of tidal debris, especially that on salt marshes, but some are found amongst barnacles and lichens on the middle shore. The life cycle has seven stages: egg, prelarva, larva, protonymph, deuteronymph, tritonymph and adult. Many coastal species but comparatively few truly littoral forms. See Hayward & Ryland (1990), Pugh & King (1988).
Suborder Astigmata: At least 4 British free-living marine species in 2 families.
Typically small (up to 0.8mm) and with a weakly sclerotised integument. There are two major groups within the Suborder, one parasitic and the other fungivorous/detritivorous. Littoral species occur on salt marshes, amongst tidal debris or in empty barnacle shells on the middle shore. The life cycle has six (or seven) stages: egg, (prelarva), larva, protonymph, sessile hypopus, tritonymph and adult. See Hayward & Ryland (1990), Pugh & King (1988).

Sub-Phylum ATELOCERATA

With over a million living species, this taxon comprises the animals generally known as insects, centipedes and millipedes. The sub-phylum has been termed 'Uniramia' in recent years, but Kukalová-Peck (1992) (see Shear, 1992) has demonstrated that name to be based on a misconception.

They are small to medium-sized, bilaterally symmetrical, metamerically somited, animals with apparently uniramous limbs and a jointed, chitinous, exoskeleton, that is moulted periodically to permit growth. The body comprises a presomital acron, a postsomital telson, and from 19 to 200 intervening somites, almost all of which may bear at least one pair of limbs. The head bears a single pair of antennae, a pair of palpless mandibles (jaws), and one or two pairs of maxillae (accessory jaws). Almost all of the twenty thousand, or so, British species are terrestrial (see Tilling, 1987) but some 130 may, possibly, be considered marine.

Super-Class Myriapoda
Ateloceratans in which there is no division of the trunk somites into thorax and abdomen. Typically these somites are numerous and each bears a pair of walking legs. Centipedes, millipedes, pill millipedes etc. Almost all are terrestrial. Seven British species may be considered marine.

Class Pauropoda: 4 British marine species in 1 family.
Very small, up to two millimetres long, blind soil-dwelling animals with uniquely branched antennae. Body adorned with long bristles. The tiny (0.2mm) nymphs hatch with only three pairs of legs and attain the full adult complement of 10 pairs after a series of moults. Very common in the soil, but typically overlooked because of their small size. Roth & Brown (1976) recorded *Allopauropus thalassopholus*, *A. danicus*, *A. littoralis* and *Thalassopauropus vermyi* under rocks or bark embedded in intertidal sand.

Class Diplopoda
Millipedes have elongate cylindrical bodies, formed of numerous similar somites, behind the head. All but the first four trunk somites are fused into pairs. Each 'diplosomite' thus has two pairs of legs. There are fifty-three British species, all bar one of them are terrestrial, although Hayward & Ryland (1990) list four others, all with a predominantly terrestrial distribution, which have been found on the shore.

Order **Julida**: 1 British marine species.
The pale greenish-white millipede *Thalassiobates littoralis* has about 40 somites and reaches 12mm (males) or 17mm (females) in length. It is a truly intertidal animal, rarely recorded, but known from Grange-over-Sands, the Isle of Man, Slapton Sands and Blakeney Point. See Blower (1985).

J. H. CROTHERS

Class Chilopoda

Centipedes have elongate, dorso-ventrally flattened bodies, formed of numerous somites behind the head. There are forty-seven British species in three Orders. All bar three of them are terrestrial.

Order **Geophilida**: 3 British marine species in 1 family.

Hydroschendyla submarina is typically found in intertidal rock crevices whilst *Strigamia maritima* and *Geophilus fucorum* are often found together, around high-water mark, in crevices under seaweed. These centipedes are eyeless, with slender 14-articulated antennae, and have long thin bodies of about 50 somites.

Super-Class Hexapoda (Insecta)

Insects are ateloceratans in which the body somites are divided into three tagmata: head, thorax and abdomen. Typically, the thorax has three somites, each of which bears a pair of legs (at least in the adult). Except in the Order Collembola, the abdomen is without appendages and is, typically, 11-somited. The twenty thousand British species are mostly terrestrial (see Tilling, 1987), some live in fresh water, and very few are truly marine. See Hayward & Ryland (1990; 1995).

Class Collembola

Order **Arthroploena**: 18 British marine or coastal species.

Springtails are small (<3mm) wingless insects with short, four-sectioned antennae and an abdomen of only six somites. Typically, the abdomen bears a paired attachment organ (ventral lobe) on the underside of the first somite and a springing organ (furcula) on the underside of the fourth somite, although this is reduced or absent in some species. There is no larval stage and all the (5 or 6) immature stages (instars) appear like miniature adults. There are approximately three hundred British species, mostly in soil or leaf litter, feeding on dead or dying plant material. Several of the species listed by Hayward & Ryland (1990; 1995) are coastal rather than marine, although others, including *Anurida maritima*, are truly intertidal. This animal, dark blue in colour, is abundant and widespread on the upper and middle rocky shore, often seen walking over the surface on sunny days, or caught in the surface film of rock pools. Disconcertingly, this springtail has no spring! See Joose (1967).

Class Apterygota

Order **Archaeognatha**: 4 British marine species in 1 family.

Three-pronged bristle tails are wingless insects with long antennae, a spindle shaped body, and three long tails (anal cerci) at the end of their eleven-somited body. The central tail is longer than the outer two. *Petrobius* species, the commonest marine genus, are inhabitants of rock crevices at around high water mark of, mainly sheltered, shores from which they descend the shore to feed intertidally at low tide by night. See Delaney (1954).

Class Pterygota

Insects in which the adult, typically, has two pairs of wings – borne on the second and third thoracic somites. The decision as to whether, or not, any particular species of flying insect should be considered part of the marine fauna is particularly subjective. Almost any insect which occurs in freshwater may occasionally be found in brackish water, and adults of almost any coastal species may be casual visitors to the shore at low tide. The following comments are restricted to those which, at some stage in their life cycle, are essentially linked with the intertidal zone. None is sublittoral. See Foster & Treherne (1976).

No mention is made here of the parasites of sea birds, which are regarded as terrestrial invertebrates because their transmission stage occurs on land.

Order **Anoplura**: 1 British marine species.

Sucking lice are wingless ectoparasites of mammals, with piercing/sucking mouthparts and the thoracic somites fused together. There is no metamorphosis in the life cycle. *Echinophthirius horridus* is widespread on both grey and common seals. See Murray (1976).

Order **Hemiptera**: 2 British marine species in the same family.

Bugs form a large group of insects with sucking mouthparts. Of nearly eighteen hundred British species, only *Saldula palustris*; and *Aepophilus bonnairei*; (Saldidae) are regular inhabitants of the intertidal zone – the former being found on mudflats and the latter in rock crevices under fucoid algae. See Polhemus (1976); Scudder (1976); Hayward & Ryland (1990).

Order **Trichoptera**: 1 British marine species.

Only two species of caddis larvae are known to live in water with a salt content significantly above that of freshwater. One of those lives in New Zealand and the other, *Limnephilus affinis*, is British. The larvae can tolerate brackish water up to 24‰. See Leader (1976).

Order **Coleoptera**: less than 10 British marine species.

There are more than four thousand British species of beetles. About a hundred or more of them, in 27 families, have been found intertidally but most of these are essentially terrestrial animals. The most committed marine species are a few carabids (especially *Aepus marinus, Aepopsis robinii, Cillenus laterale, Dicheirotrichus gustavii* and some *Nebria* sp.) and staphylinids (*Bledius spectabilis, Diglotta marina* and *Micralymma marina*) but there are several more on salt marshes. See Elliott in Hayward & Ryland (1990).

Order **Diptera**: At least 46 British marine species in 21 families.

There are more than six thousand British species of two-winged, true flies, almost all of which are terrestrial or freshwater animals. However, the wingless, legless larvae of a few species[21] are genuine marine animals, feeding, for example: amongst the lichen *Lichina pygmaea* (Tipulidae, Dolichopodidae); inside the cylindrical fronds of the green alga *Enteromorpha* (Chironomidae and Tipulidae); amongst rotting seaweed on the drift line (Coelopidae, Empididae, Sphaeroceridae, Muscidae) or on the pelt of seals (Muscidae, Sphaeroceridae). Larvae of *Villeneuvia aestum* (Muscidae) and all four species of *Aphrosylus* (Dolichopodidae) are carnivores, preying on barnacles and other sedentary animals. See Smith (1989), Dobson (1976) for Coelopidae; Hashimoto (1976) for Chironomidae.

---

[21] Most members of the families listed here (words ending in -idae) are terrestial animals. Only a few species occur on the shore.

Phylum PYCNOGONIDA

Sea spiders are an entirely marine group, sometimes regarded as a Class within the sub-phylum Chelicerata of the Arthropoda. I have followed Hayward & Ryland (1990; 1995) and Hayward *et al.* (1996) and treat them as a separate phylum. Head and trunk are discrete, i.e. not fused together, and there is no carapace. Opisthosoma very small and unsomited. The head has a cylindrical proboscis and bears three pairs of appendages – chelicerae, pedipalps and ovigerous legs (used by the male for carrying eggs). The trunk has four somites, each bearing a pair of walking legs at the end of a lateral extension (trunk process). All sea spiders are predators of bryozoans or hydroids. No generally acceptable scheme has yet been found for grouping the 10 families into Orders. Nineteen British species in six families. See King (1974; 1986) and Hayward & Ryland (1990; 1995).

Phylum LOBOPODIA
Sub-Phylum TARDIGRADA

World-wide, there are some four hundred species of water bear but only seventy-four have been recorded in Britain. These are small (50-1200 μm long) multicellular animals most commonly seen in the surface water of mosses, lichens and liverworts. The marine forms are mostly found in the interstitial water between sand grains although *Echiniscoides sigismundi* has been recorded on barnacles, in mussels and on green algae. The name 'water bears' reflects their lumbering gait. The squat cylindrical body bears four pairs of stubby, unjointed, fleshy legs; each ending in claws. The head is not clearly demarcated from the trunk and both ends of the body are bluntly rounded. The mucopolysaccharide/protein cuticle may be smooth, or ornamented with spines, or divided into plates. The gut runs the whole length of the body but there are no respiratory or circulatory systems.

The unfamiliar taxon Lobopodia has been proposed (see Shear, 1992) for the various groups of 'walking worms' – Onychophora, Tardigrada, Pentasomida and various fossils including the formerly-mysterious *Hallucigenia* from the Burgess Shale.

Class Heterotardigrada;
Order **Arthrotardigrada**: 16 British marine species in 2 families.
The head bears cephalic appendages and lateral cephalic cirri. The legs have adhesive discs, or 'toes' see Morgan & King (1976), Morgan & O'Reilly (1988), Hayward & Ryland (1990, but not 1995).

Phylum CHAETOGNATHA

Arrow worms are translucent, even transparent, macroscopic members of the marine zooplankton, world wide. They form a neat homogenous group (70 species have been described) which has 'resisted' the attempts of taxonomists to link it with any other. The body is divided into head, trunk and tail by internal partitions. The head is typically rounded and connected to the trunk by a slightly narrowed neck. The gut is straight, from the subterminal mouth to an anus at the base of the tail.

Chaetognaths typically feed on copepods, but amphipods, euphausiids, ostracods, medusae, polychaetes, tunicates and fish larvae have all been taken. Some species may also take phytoplankton. Prey items are caught by a system of grasping hooks and teeth around the mouth as the head is rapidly everted from its covering hood, in an ambush. The body is typically held rigidly in a straight line and movement is generally by a sequence of flicks and glides between periods of hovering in the water.

Arrow worms are hermaphrodite and fertilisation is by copulation via spermatophores. Fertilised eggs are released directly into the sea. There is no true larval stage, although that word is used for the youngest juveniles, and development is continuous. Longevity from 6 weeks to 2 years. All are marine. All but the benthic genus *Spadella* (of which, *S. cephaloptera* is found in British waters) are planktonic and some species (particularly *Sagitta elegans* and *Sagitta setosa*) are valuable as indicators of different water masses.

Pierrot-Bults & Chidgey (1988) list 19 species, in 5 genera, from the North-east Atlantic and around the British Isles.

Phylum HEMICHORDATA

Hemichordates are of two main types, which differ considerably in their body forms and life styles. Both are bilaterally-symmetrical, unsomited benthic marine animals with their body divided into three regions – proboscis, collar and trunk. The collar bears the mouth (ventrally) may have up to nine pairs of arms (dorsally), each with numerous small ciliated tentacles. The sexes are separate: fertilisation is external and the eggs typically hatch into a ciliated larva. As their name suggests, these animals share a number of features with the phylum Chordata. They lack a notochord but do have a perforated pharynx and some may have a post-anal tail, although it is not used for swimming. See Hayward & Ryland (1990; 1995).

Class Enteropneusta: 9 British species in 2 families.
Acorn worms are solitary, freely mobile, worm-shaped animals that can reach three metres in length. They lack tentacles on the collar. The gut extends from a mouth, on the collar, to a terminal anus. There are many pharyngeal slits, new ones being produced throughout life. The body comprises a long proboscis, short collar, and very long trunk. They live in 'U'-shaped, mucous-lined, burrows and show marked powers of asexual regeneration. Food is collected by the proboscis cilia. *Balanoglossus*, *Glossobalanus* and company were favourite examples in systematic text-books.

Class Pterobranchia
Order **Rhabdopleurida**: at least 2 British species.
These are minute colonial sessile animals, living in tubes (ca. 0.2mm diameter) attached to the substratum. The body is sac-like, bearing arms on the collar, and with a stalk connecting it to other zooids. The gut is 'U'-shaped, bringing the anus onto the collar as well. There is a single pair of pharyngeal slits.

Phylum ECHINODERMATA

Echinoderms are free-living unsomited marine animals with a five-rayed symmetry; in effect, radial in some and bilateral in others. There is no head, and no brain; nor are there any excretory organs. The body is supported by a sub-epidermal skeleton of calcareous spicules or plates, onto which may articulate a system of spines or other structures (pedicellariae, etc.) that serve to protect or cleanse the epithelium. The water vascular system is filled with essentially sea water and comprises a ring canal around the oesophagus, five radial canals, and a calcified stone canal which typically terminates at a porous madreporite, through which water may be exchanged with the sea outside. A distal series of outpushings from the radial canals, form podia, tube feet or tentacles, that are operated hydraulically. Tube feet are often the locomotory organs, but movement may also be achieved using spines or arms.

In most species, the mouth is in the centre of the lower surface and the anus, if present, in the centre of the upper. Nervous and blood systems comprise circumoesophageal rings with five ambulacral elements radiating from them. Gaseous exchange is effected through papillate extensions of the water vascular system.

The sexes are typically separate but fertilisation is external. Development of the embryo may be direct but typically involves a planktonic larva which bears long sinuous tracts of cilia. Patterns shown by these ciliary tracts are characteristic of the different Classes, and have attracted particular names.

Representatives of five of the six Classes of living Echinoderms are known from British seas. It is not likely that any sea daisies (Class Concentricycloidea) will be recorded for all known examples have been collected on dead wood in very deep water. See Pearse *et al.* (1987).

For further identification of British species see Hayward & Ryland (1990), and Picton (1993).

Class Crinoidea

Most sea lilies are attached to the substratum by a stalk from the aboral surface of their body, but no permanently-attached forms occur in British waters. They are suspension feeders, catching their food by tube feet arranged along their five moveable arms. In all British species, each arm divides into 2 at the base, so that the animal appears to have ten arms. All bear numerous side pinnules. The ciliated grooves, along the upper side of each groove, bear food to the upwardly-directed mouth. Mouth and anus are both on the upper side of the body.

Order **Comatulida**: 3 British species in a single family.

Adult feather stars are able to swim using their 10 feathery arms, although they may temporarily attach themselves to the substratum by somited unbranched processes, called cirri, which arise from the central plate on the underside of the disk. The vitellaria larva metamorphoses into an attached stalked (pentacrinoid) juvenile stage from which the adult breaks free. *Antedon bifida* is the best-known species.

Class Asteroidea

Starfish, have a star-shaped body, with a spiny or smooth surface. The five (or more) tapering arms extend from a large central disc, typically without any distinct break between arm and disc. Locomotion is effected by movement of the tube feet, which lie in an ambulacral furrow along the underside of each arm and may, or may not, have terminal attachment suckers. The mouth is on the underside (which is thus called the oral surface) and the anus, if present, on the upper (aboral) surface. The calcareous skeleton is diffuse, although the edges of the arms may be sharply marked by distinctive ossicles known as marginal plates. The general outer surface is typically protected by short spines of various types, and equipped with pedicellariae (small stalked, almost robotic, jawed structures used for grooming). Asteroid pedicellariae are of two types: crossed, in which the jaw ossicles have a scissors-like action; and straight, with a forceps action. Some species show direct development, others have bipinnaria and/or brachiolaria larvae. See Southward (1972); Hayward & Ryland (1990; 1995).

Order **Phanerozonida**: 5 British species in 4 families.

Starfish with conspicuous marginal plates along the sides of their five arms. The pedicellariae are simple, never crossed. In the burrowing families (Astropectinidae; and Luidiidae) the tube feet have no suckers; in the others Poraniidae and Goniasteridae, which resemble cushion stars, they do.

Order **Spinulosida**: 8 British species in 3 families.

Starfish with groups of spines on their upper surface. Pedicellariae are rarely present and, if so, are simple. Their tube feet have suckers. Cushion stars (Asterinidae) have a large disc and five short arms; members of the Echinasteridae have a small disc and five long cylindrical arms; whilst sunstars (Solasteridae) have a large disc and between seven and thirteen arms.

Order **Forcipulatida**: 4 British species in 2 families.

Starfish with complex crossed pedicellariae, at least on the aboral surface; straight ones are typically present at well. Tube feet have suckers. All British species typically have five arms.

Class Ophiuroidea

Brittle stars have a star-shaped body, with a spiny or smooth surface. There is a sharp demarcation between the small disc and the five (very brittle) arms. The tube feet, used for feeding rather than for locomotion, are without terminal attachment suckers. Locomotion is effected by moving the arms. The mouth is on the underside (which is thus called the oral surface); there is no anus. The calcareous skeleton is well developed and occupies most of the body volume. The general outer surface is typically protected by spines of various types, but there are no pedicellariae. The larval stage is called an ophiopluteus. Only two of the three Orders occur in British seas. See Southward (1972); Hayward & Ryland (1990). Classification revised by Smith, Paterson & Lafay (1995).

Order **Euryalae**: 2 British species in 2 families.

Brittlestars in which the arms are typically coiled. *Gorgonocephalus caputmedusa* has extensively branched arms but the five, very long, arms of *Asteronyx loveni* are single.

Order **Ophiurae**: 19 British species in 5 families.

Brittlestars in which the five arms are not branched and are incapable of much coiling.

Class Echinoidea

Most sea urchins have a globular body, without arms, and with a well-developed calcareous skeleton of large plates fused to form a rigid test. In the region of the mouth, within the test, there is often a complex dental apparatus, known as 'Aristotle's Lantern', which operates five teeth (jaws) which project through the mouth. Tube feet lie in five ambulacral areas, each of two rows, extending from the central, ventral mouth to the dorsal madreporite. Locomotion is effected either by the tube feet alone, or in conjunction with the long, moveable spines. Echinoid pedicellariae are of five types. Some species show direct development, others have an echinopluteus larvae. See Southward (1972); Hayward & Ryland (1990; 1995).

Order **Diadematoida**: 5 British species in 3 families.
Sea urchins in which the test is circular, spherical or flattened. The anus is central on the dorsal (aboral) surface. Pedicellariae of four types. Aristotle's lantern is well-developed.

Order **Clypeastroida**: 1 British species.
Echinocyamus pusillus is a burrowing sea urchin (up to 15mm long) in which the test is bilaterally-symmetrical, somewhat elongated and flattened. The anus lies on the under (oral) side, posterior to the mouth. Pedicellariae are of three types, but inconspicuous. Spines and tube feet are small. Aristotle's lantern is well-developed.

Order **Spatangoida**: 5 British species in 1 family.
Heart urchins are burrowing sea urchins with a bilaterally-symmetrical, elongated and flattened test. The mouth is 'anterior' and the anus 'posterior'. A ring of ciliated spines (the sub-anal fasciole), lying below the anus, encloses a ring of 'sanitary-building' tube feet. No Aristotle's lantern.

Class Holothuroidea

Sea cucumbers are bilaterally-symmetrical elongate, sausage-shaped animals, without arms, having the mouth at one end and the anus at the other. The calcareous skeleton is reduced to discrete microscopic ossicles. Tube feet lie in five ambulacra; three of them, in contact with the substratum, form a 'ventral' sole, and the others 'dorsal'. Locomotion is effected by the tube feet. Around the mouth are between eight and thirty, often branched, tentacles for the collection of food. Respiratory trees may open into the rectum, irrigated with sea water by cloacal pumping. Some species show direct development, others have an auricularia, doliolaria or vitellaria larva. See Southward (1972); Hayward & Ryland (1990; 1995).

Order **Aspidochirotida**: 2 British species in 2 families.
Sea cucumbers with between fifteen and thirty shield-shaped tentacles. Only the ventral tube feet are locomotory, dorsal ones form papillae. Respiratory trees present.

Order **Dendrochirotida**: 12 British species in 2 families.
Sea cucumbers with between ten and thirty highly-branched, retractile tentacles. Tube feet and respiratory trees present.

Order **Apodida**: 5 British species in a single family.
Elongate, worm-like, sea cucumbers. British species have either eleven or twelve tentacles. There are no tube feet or respiratory trees.

Phylum CHORDATA

The Phylum Chordata has three extant sub-phyla: Urochordata, Cephalochordata and Vertebrata. The latter are outside the scope of this work. Members of the two invertebrate sub-phyla are clearly distinct from that group – in that they lack a vertebral column – yet have some features which suggest a relationship with vertebrates. The most obvious of these are the presence (at any rate for part of the life cycle) of a notochord, a tubular dorsal nerve cord and perforations of the pharynx comparable to the gill slits of fish. Of course, most adult vertebrates have no notochord or gill slits – but these structures are present in the embryo.

Sub-Phylum UROCHORDATA

All urochordates are marine, with a body encased in an external fibrous test or tunic (hence their alternative name of Tunicata) containing cellulose. Their larvae have features which seem to show relationships with vertebrates, but there are few signs in the adults which may be sessile or free-swimming, solitary or colonial. The body is unsomited and typically lacks an obvious head. It is typically dominated by a relatively-enormous pharynx, perforated by numerous slits (stigmata), by means of which they filter feed. Water enters through a brachial siphon by ciliary pumping and passes through the stigmata. Any particles in that water become trapped in mucus whilst the filtered water leaves the body via the atrial siphon. The gut is short, and often U-shaped, with the anus opening into the atrial siphon.

Adults are typically simultaneous hermaphrodites and asexual budding is common – typically resulting in the formation of colonies which may be formed within a common tunic.

Class Ascidiacea

Adult sea squirts are sessile animals, filter feeding through the walls of their pharynx. Branchial and atrial siphons are close together. They may grow singly, or in colonies produced by asexual budding from the founding individual. The life cycle is straightforward, without an alteration of sexual and asexual generations. The eggs hatch as a tadpole larva (so called because its shape resembles that of an amphibian larva) about 1mm long. They do not feed and most settle to metamorphose within a few hours. Running the length of their tail is a notochord – a row of some 40-42 cylindrical cells with large vacuoles, enclosed in a sheath of connective tissue fibres. On each side are three rows of muscle cells, which contract alternately to bend the tail from side to side. Dorsal to the notochord is a tubular nerve cord, swollen at the anterior end where it contains two simple sense organs – probably a light receptor and a tilt receptor. See Millar (1970).

Order **Aplousobranchia**: 22 British species in 3 families.
Colonial sea squirts, in which the body is divided into thorax and abdomen, or thorax, abdomen and postabdomen. The wall of the pharynx is not folded and has up to 20 rows of stigmata. Gonads lie in the intestinal loop.

Order **Phlebobranchia**: 12 British species in 5 families.
Mostly solitary sea squirts, often large, in which the body never has a postabdomen. There are internal longitudinal bars on the wall of the pharynx. Gonads lie in the intestinal loop.

Order **Pleurogona**: 26 British species in 3 families.

Mostly solitary sea squirts, in which the body is not divided into regions. The wall of the pharynx is folded longitudinally and bears internal longitudinal bars. Gonads arise from the atrial wall, alongside the pharynx.

Class Thaliacea

In these planktonic animals the branchial and atrial siphons are at the opposite ends of a barrel-shaped, or fusiform, body. The exhalant water current provides the propulsive force for movement. They are either colonial or alternate between solitary and colonial forms. See Fraser (1981).

Order **Pyrosomida**: 2 doubtfully British species in a single family.

Colonies, up to 2m in length, in which the zooids all lie in a common cylindrical test, open at one end. The branchial siphon of each zooid draws water into the colony from the outer surface whilst the atrial siphon discharges into the common atrium. No free-swimming larva.

Order **Doliolida**: 3 British species in a single family.

In doliolids, the solitary generation reproduces sexually to form an asexually-multiplying colonial generation of polymorphic individuals. The thin gelatinous tunic is transparent, allowing the 8 or 9 hoops of muscle, encircling the body, to be visible externally. The pharynx may have many stigmata. There is a tadpole larval stage.

Order **Salpida**: 12 British species in a single family.

In salps, the colonial generation reproduces asexually to form chains which separate to yield the solitary sexual individuals. The gelatinous tunic is thick but it is possible to see the incomplete circles of muscle encircling the body. Pharynx with two large stigmata. Viviparous without a larval stage.

Class Larvacea

Small, solitary neotenous planktonic animals, with a large tail and generally somewhat resemble the 'tadpole' larval stage of ascidians. The animal secretes, and lives within, a gelatinous 'house', which provides both a protective covering and a large area for filtering food from the surrounding water. Currents, made by movements of the tail, draw water into the house through a system of filters and out through an exhalant aperture. This process draws the house, very slowly, through the water. For use in emergency, or when the filters are clogged, there may be an escape hatch through which the animal can leave the old 'house' and begin to secrete a new one. The houses rarely survive in a plankton net, being reduced to unrecognisable mush.

Order **Copelat**a: 4 British species in 2 families.

Pharynx with two stigmata. The tail, which incorporates a notochord and a nerve cord, is attached to the short axis of the body giving an overall shape more like a hammer than a tadpole. Adults are hermaphrodite. Fertilisation is external and there is a tadpole larval stage, very like that of ascidians. They feed on the nannoplankton and are, in turn, fed on by many carnivorous plankters, especially fish larvae. Only *Oikopleura dioica* and *Fritillaria borealis* can be considered abundant in British inshore waters. See Fraser (1981).

Sub-Phylum CEPHALOCHORDATA

Order **Amphioxida**: 1 British species.

The lancelet, *Branchiostoma lanceolatum*, is a cigar-shaped free-swimming, benthic, laterally-compressed, marine animal, that grows up to 60mm in length. The body tapers at each end and is supported by a notochord, extending its whole length. The hollow dorsal nerve cord, which is nearly as long, does not dilate anteriorly to form a brain. The somitally-arranged muscle blocks are clearly visible through the very thin skin. The animal is a detritivore, filter feeding material from the sand and gravel in which it lives. Sexes are separate, fertilisation is external and there is no larval stage. There are only 20, or so, species, world-wide, in this sub-phylum.

GLOSSARY

Aboral: On the side of the body opposite to the mouth (contrast **oral**).

Acanthella larva: The intermediate larval stage(s) of an acanthocephalan parasite, living in the body of its intermediate host.

Acanthor larva: The hooked, first larval stage of an acanthocephalan parasite. It is an internal parasite, hatching from the egg when he latter is eaten by its intermediate host.

Acicula (pl. aciculae): An internal chitinous rod supporting the parapodial lobe in some polychaete worms.

Acron: The basic arthropodan body plan typically comprises a presomital **acron**, a post-somital telson and an intervening series of somites organised into three tagmata, head, thorax and abdomen.

Adductor muscles: Muscles which close the valves of a bivalve mollusc. Their position is indicated on the inside of an empty bivalve shell by the presence of **muscle scars**.

Adumbral: Underneath. The inner, lower surface of a jelly-fish's bell.

Ambulacral: Used for walking.

Amphids: Paired chemosensory organs on the head of a nematode worm. They may be of a pocket-type, transverse slit-type, circular-type or spiral-type with varying numbers of turns.

Anal cerci: Hair-like processes projecting from the skin around the anus in insects.

Anastomosing: Branching and re-joining, thereby producing a mat-like structure - usually of fine tubes.

Ancestrula: The founding zooid (individual) of a bryozoan colony.

Annulus (pl. annuli): A ring. The term is generally used to describe a cylindrical structure (often a worm) where rings on the skin do not indicate somitation in the body within.

Antenna (pl. antennae): A mobile, flagellate sensory appendage arising from the head. Crustaceans have two pairs of antennae and, in that taxon, the term is restricted to the posterior pair (Second Antennae).

Antennule (pl. antennules): The first antenna of a crustacean.

Apical: At or of, the apex or tip.

Aquiferous: Carrying water.

Arms: The locomotory limbs of radially-symmetrical echinoderms – starfish, brittle stars and feather stars.

Asterose: Star shaped.

Asters: Stars.

Ateloceratans: Members of the sub-phylum Atelocerata.

Axial: aligned along the axis, or mid-line, of a structure.

Basis: Limb segment immediately distal to the **coxa**, in a crustacean.

Benthos: Animals living on the sea bed (adj. benthic).

Bi-laterally symmetrical: Symmetry in which only one diameter splits the structure into two mirror-image halves. i.e. left and right sides of the body are mirror images of each other. (contrast **radially symmetrical**).

Biramous: With two arms. When describing crustacean limbs, this term reflects the primitive condition where each one, be it **antenna**, **pereiopod**, **pleopod**, or **maxilliped** or whatever, is composed of two elements – an inner **endopodite** and an outer **exopodite**.

Bristle: A rod, probably pointed, projecting from the surface of an animal. The mid-point of the cilium-hair-bristle-spine continuum.

Buccal cavity: A space immediately inside the mouth.

Byssus: Protein threads secreted by certain bivalve mollusc species to anchor the animal to the substratum.

Calyx: A term, borrowed from floral descriptions, for the globular body of an entoproct zooid.

Calyptosis larva: One of the post-naupliar stages in the development of euphausiid crustacea. See **crustacean larvae**.

Captaculae: The feeding appendages of scaphopods.

Carapace: A fold of exoskeleton which extends from the head out and over some or all of the thoracic somites.

Carcinoecium: An animal colony formed around a living crab.

Carpus: Limb segment immediately proximal to the **propus** in crustacea.

Caudal: Of the tail.

Caudal cirrus: A small, tail-like extension at the posterior end of the body.

Cavernicolous: Living in caves.

Cephalic: Of the head.

Cephalic furrow, groove or slit: A longitudinal, oblique or transverse depression in the cephalic epidermis of a nemertean worm, sometimes very deep, lined by a ciliated epithelium which normally lacks gland cells;

the furrows are paired and their distribution on the head may be of taxonomic importance; typically, although not always, the cerebral sensory organs open into the furrows.

Cephalic lobe: The rounded, semi-circular, heart-shaped or flattened anterior tip of a nemertean worm, clearly distinguishable from the trunk. It is not strictly equivalent to a head as it typically does not contain the cerebral ganglia.

Cephalisation: Head formation - the fusion of somites at the front end of the body into a head.

Cephalothorax: A fusion of some or all of the thoracic somites with the head.

Cerata: Outgrowths from the **mantle** on the dorsal surface of nudibranch sea slugs.

Cerebral ganglion (pl. ganglia): The brain lobes, characteristically consisting of dorsal and ventral pairs of cerebral lobes, in close connection with each other, linked by transverse commissures. Chela (**pl. chelae**): a claw or pincer.

Chelate: In the form of a claw or pincer.

Chlorocruorin: A green blood pigment in some annelid worms.

Choanocytes: Cells lining the canals and chambers of the aquiferous system in sponges, creating the necessary water circulation by beating their flagella. They are almost identical to free-living Choanoflagellates.

Chordoid larva: The dispersal stage of *Symbion pandora* in the phylum Cycliophora, formed on the degeneration of the fertilised adult female.

Chromatophore: A pigment-containing cell. These may be diffuse and branching or concentrated and spot-like, the intensity of colour being dependent on the diffusion of the pigment.

Ciliated: Covered in cilia.

Cilium (pl. cilia): A very fine mobile hair. Cilia can create water currents by beating sequentially, and can cause very small animals to swim or crawl. The fine end of the cilium-hair-bristle-spine continuum.

Circumapical: Around the apex, or tip.

Class: A group of similar Orders.

Clitellum: An area on an adult oligochaete worm that looks as though as extra piece of tubing has been attached over the normal worm's body.

Cnida (pl. cnidae) (n.): Stinging or adhesive organelles unique to the phylum Cnidaria. Sometimes called thread- or sting-capsules. A cnida is a secreted, essentially intracellular capsule within which is a coiled and folded

tubule which everts and straightens on discharge. The cell secreting it is called a cnidocyte (termed cnidoblast when immature).

Throughout the phylum, different kinds of cnidae are used in prey capture, defence and attachment. The three categories, each fulfilling a range of these functions, are nematocyst, spirocyst and ptychocyst. Each is secreted respectively by a special cnidocyte - nematocyte, spirocyte or ptychocyte. When the secreting cells are immature, i.e., when their respective cnidae are not yet fully formed, they are termed nematoblast, spiroblast or ptychoblast.

Cnidocyte: See **cnida**.

Coelenteron: The central cavity or gut of a cnidarian polyp or medusa; often abbreviated to 'enteron'.

Coenchymatous: Joined together in tissue contact, as in the coenchymatous mass formed from the fusion of anastomosing hydroid **stolons**.

Coenosarc: The tube of living hydroid tissue within the perisarc (outer skeleton). Essentially, the living material connecting the various polyps in a colony.

Collagenous: Made of collagen.

Colonial: A species in which new 'individuals' form asexually from the founding individual, but do not completely separate from each other so that the various **polyps** or **zooids** remain in tissue contact (in contrast to a **solitary** animal).

Columella: The 'little column' that forms the central spire of a gastropod shell.

Corallum: The external calcareous shell / case of a coral.

Cordyli: Minute club-shaped structures hanging from the bell margin of some medusae, probably sensory in function.

Corona: A little crown. A crown of tentacles or the wheel-organ of a rotiferan.

Coronal groove (of a jellyfish): A linear indentation encircling the bell, suggesting that a draw string has been pulled around it too tightly.

Coxa: The most proximal segment of a crustacean limb, being the segment which is joined to the body of the animal.

Creeping: The slow extension of a soft-bodied colonial animal over the substratum. (cf. **encrusting**).

Crustacean larvae: Some crustaceans lay many small eggs, each with a small supply of yolk. Others lay fewer, larger yolky eggs. Two general rules apply : The smaller the supply of yolk, the earlier is the stage at which the larva hatches; and, The head region develops first and posterior somites are developed later so that the youngest larvae have fewest legs, and the oldest the most.

Typically, the egg hatches into a **nauplius** larva, with three pairs of appendages (antennules, antennae and mandibles). There is a medial simple eye, a large labrum and a pair of frontal organs in the form of papillae or filaments.

There follows a succession of larval stages in which more and more somites and limbs are added, although not necessarily in the adult order from front to rear. Changes in form occur at each moult.

In branchiopods, the adult form is reached gradually, by the addition of a few somites at a time from a growth zone just in front of the telson. In gradual development of this kind, the successive instars are not sufficiently different to warrant stadial names.

More commonly, however, growth is metamorphic and more abrupt changes occur at some moults. Rather confusingly, particular names have been given to these latter stages in some groups of Crustacea. These names are historical accidents, being the generic names assigned to the larvae before the link with their adult forms had been established.

In a zoea larva, the main divisions of the body are obvious and the animal swims, mainly, by means of its biramous maxillipeds. Other thoracic legs are added, posteriorly, in later zoeal stages. In those crustacea which have the final **megalopa** stage, the adult body form is previewed, although even those of crabs swim by using the abdominal appendages.

Crustacean limbs: Each appendage consists of a basal protopodite (attached to the body by a coxopodite (often abbreviated to coxa) from which arise an inner, endopodite, and an outer, exopodite, both multiarticulate. Each of these three limb sections may bear projections, termed respectively epipodites (on the basopodite), endites (on the endopodite) and exites (on the exopodite), some of which may function as gills.

Of a crab's 20-somited body, the first 6 form the head.

Somite 1 has no limbs
Somite 2 has the 1st antennae
Somite 3 has the 2nd antennae
Somite 4 has the mandibles
Somite 5 has the 1st maxillae
Somite 6 has the 2nd maxillae
the next 8 form the thorax
Somite 7 has the 1st maxillipeds

Somite 8 has the 2nd maxillipeds
Somite 9 has the 3rd maxillipeds
Somite 10 has the chelae
Somite 11 has the 2nd pereiopods
Somite 12 has the 3rd pereiopods
Somite 13 has the 4th pereiopods
the remainder form the abdomen and bear pleopods (in the female) all except the last (telson) which has no legs.

Cystacanth larva: The final larval stage of an acanthocephalan parasite, living in the body of its intermediate host until the latter is eaten by a suitable vertebrate final host.

Dermis: Skin. The tissue layer between the epidermis and the body wall musculature in nemertean worms.

Diactine: A monaxon sponge spicule pointed at both ends. See **spicule**.

Disc: The central area of a starfish, brittle star or feather star, bearing the mouth and anus, and to which the **arms** are attached.

Distal: The end furthest away from the point of attachment (opposite of **proximal**).

Dorsal: The upper side (contrast **ventral**).

Echinopluteus larve: The dispersal stage of a sea urchin.

Encrustation: A rigid supporting structure (skeleton?) of a colonial animal or red alga over the substratum.

Encrusting: Forming an encrustation.

Endites: See **Crustacean limbs**.

Endogenous Living in the substratum.

Epipodite: See **Crustacean limbs**.

Equivalve: The two valves of a bivalve shell are (or are very nearly) mirror images of each other.

Exogenous Living at or above the surface of the substratum.

Exopodite (or exopod): The outer branch of a crustacean limb, normally found arising from the basis of the **maxillipeds** and **pereiopods**. Normally shorter than the main limb (the endopodite), and often setose. The exopods of the abdominal pleopods are leaf-like in shape.

Exhalent siphon: A tube through which the animal blows out water. (Contrast **inhalent siphon**).

Exites: See **Crustacean limbs**.

Exoskeleton: A skeleton outside the body. The term is most often used for the protective coating of arthropods.

External shell (of a mollusc or brachiopod): A shell which is fundamentally outside the body, although it may be partially enveloped in the mantle when the animal is active. The animal can typically withdraw inside it, so it is used for protection as well as for skeletal support.

Exumbral: The outer, upper surface of a jellyfish's bell.

Exuvia (Pl. Exuviae): The sloughed exoskeleton remaining after moulting.

Family: A group of similar genera.

Filiform: Like a filament i.e., thin and elongated.

Flagellum: The straight, distal portion of the antenna consisting of two or more segments.

Free-living: Living on its own, not dependent (as might be a commensal or a parasite) upon another animal or plant for survival.

Frontal: At the front of the head.

Furcilia stage: The second post-naupliar larval stage of euphausiid crustacea. See **crustacean larvae**.

Gastrozooid: See **zooid**.

Gelatinous: Like a jelly.

Genus (pl. genera): A group of similar species.

Gonochoristic: Populations composed of males and females in roughly 50:50 proportions.

Gonozoid: Brood chamber. See **zooid**.

Hair: A delicate rod projecting from the surface of an animal. The mid-point of the cilium-hair-bristle-spine continuum.

Head tentacles: Outgrowths from the head, typically with a sensory function.

Hermaphroditism: The condition whereby both male and female gametes are produced by the same individual.

Heterostrophic condition (of gastropod molluscs): When the protoconch and teloconch show different coiling patterns.

Hydranth: The polyp of a colonial hydroid.

Hydromedusa (pl. hydromedusae): The adult, little jelly fish stage, of a cnidarian hydroid.

Hydrotheca (pl. hydrothecae): A cup (theca), on the colony of a cnidarian hydroid, into which the polyp (hydranth) can be retracted.

Hyperbenthic: Living (just) above the bottom.

Hypostome: On a hydroid - the terminal region of a hydranth, on which the mouth is situated.

Incisor process: A projection of the **mandible**, normally toothed, used for cutting food particles.

Inhalent siphon: A tube through which the animal sucks in water. (Contrast **exhalent siphon**).

Inequivalve: The two valves of a bivalved shell are dissimilar in form.

Internal shell (of a mollusc): A shell totally enclosed by the mantle and used entirely for skeletal support or buoyancy.

Intertidal: The area between the high and low tide marks – sea shore.

Ischium: The crustacean limb segment nearest the **basis**, distally, and the **merus** proximally.

Lateral: Side.

Ligament: The non-living elastic structure which causes a bivalve mollusc shell to gape, opposed in life by the adductor muscle(s). It may be wholly inside the shell (**internal ligament**) with a special attachment plate (**chondrophore**) or wholly outside (**external ligament**) attached to the outer surface of the shell.

Littoral zone: The intertidal zone, generally known as the sea shore.

Lophophore: A tentacular system, more complicated than the circular ring(s) of tentacles seen in cnidarians. In its simplest form, the ring of tentacles is horseshoe-shaped: in more complicated examples the ends of the horseshoe curl in on themselves – to the left and to the right – until the whole structure resembles an open scroll in cross section. The more the ring coils, the more tentacles can be fitted in.

Lusitanian distribution: Refers to a distribution pattern which is restricted to the south west of Britain and Ireland.

Madreporite: A porous plate (usually on the dorsal, or aboral, surface] through which the water vascular system of an echinoderm communicates with the sea outside.

Manca: The juvenile stage of a woodlice.

Mandible: Crustacea have a pair of mandibles, which are mouthparts concerned with the mechanical breakdown of food. Each mandible is normally made up of a **incisor process** plus a **molar process**. A palp may be present or absent.

Mantle: The dorsal surface of a mollusc which, in shelled forms, secretes the shell. In most species it remains within the shell at all times but, in others, the edges may wrap out and over the shell of an active animal. In extreme cases they may form **parapodia** – wing like structures with which the animal may swim.

Mantle cavity: A sinus (space) within the mantle of a mollusc which generally contains the gill(s) and into which the anus opens.

Marginal: Around the edge.

Marsupium: Brood pouch.

Maxilla (pl. maxillae): Accessory mouthparts situated posterior to the **mandibles**. See **crustacean limbs**.

Maxilliped: Accessory feeding limbs situated posterior to the **maxillae**. They are involved in the handling and breakdown of food, although originally of thoracic origin. The third maxilliped is typically the least modified, and may resemble a **pereiopod** on casual inspection. See **crustacean limbs**.

Megalopa: See **crustacean larvae**.

Merus: Crustacean limb segment between the **ischium** and the **carpus**.

Mesenteries: 'Partition walls' within the enteron (coelenteron) of sea anemones and corals which increase the surface area and, thus, the efficiency of feeding.

Mesoglea: (Formerly, mesogloea) In Cnidaria, a tissue layer between epidermis and gastrodermis, usually functioning in the manner of an elaborate basement membrane and as a flexible skeleton. In medusae, it has this function in smaller organs such as tentacles and the manubrium but, across most of the umbrella, it is much thickened, muscular and contractile. It is the jelly of jellyfish.

Microscleres: The smaller spicules in the skeleton of a sponge. See **spicule**.

Molar process: A projection of the crustacean **mandible**, used for grinding down food particles.

Monaxon: See **spicule**.

Monoactine: monaxon sponge spicule pointed at one end. See **spicule**.

Monophyletic: Descended from a common ancestor.

Motile: Capable of movement.

Muscle scars: Marks on the inside of a bivalve mollusc shell indicating the attachment areas of the adductor muscles – visible because the mantle has not been in contact with the shell at this point.

Nauplius: See **crustacean larvae**.

Naupliar eye: A single, median, eye as seen, typically, in the nauplius larva of a crustacean. It may still be visible at later stages of development.

Nekton: The community of powerful swimming animals which can move at will through the water in contrast to the plankton. (adj. nektonic).

Nematocysts: See **cnida**.

Nematophores: Specialised structures housing batteries of nematocysts.

Nematotheca: In hydroids, the cup for a nematophore. See **theca**.

Nomenclature: The procedure for naming animals and plants.

Nuchal tentacles: Tentacles which arise dorsally from the head.

Ocellus: A single primitive eye spot.

Ommatidium: One of the components of a compound eye.

Onchomiracidia larva: The free-swimming larva of a monogenean parasite (fluke) that attacks fish.

Onchosphere larva: The free-swimming larva of a cestode (tapeworm).

Oostegites: The rudimentary structures from which the overlapping plates of the marsupium develop.

Operculum: A trap door that seals off the opening of a tube or shell when the animal is inside.

Oral: Of the mouth. Oral surface – the side of the body including the mouth.

Orbit: Socket-like depression which partly surrounds the eyes.

Order: A group of similar families.

Oscula: The conspicuous holes in the surface of a sponge.

Ossicles: Structures on echinoderms that have the appearance of bony plates.

Ovigerous spine: A spine to which eggs are attached.

Oviparous: Laying eggs.

Ovoviviparous: Egg development after internal fertilisation leading to the formation of young within the body of the mother, although the developing young are nourished by the egg yolk stores only and not through tissue involvement of the maternal organs.

Pallial line: A line on the inside of a bivalve mollusc's shell showing the normal extent of the animal's mantle (and visible because the outer surface of the mantle lays down the innermost layers of the shell).

Pandora larva: An asexual brooding larva of *Symbion pandora* in the phylum Cycliophora, locally free-swimming but settling on the same host, containing new feeding stages.

Pallial sinus: An indentation in the **pallial line** of certain bivalves, indicating the area in which the animals siphons are kept, when retracted.

Parenchyma: The body-packing tissue, filling the space between the body wall layers and the internal organs, composed of connective tissues.

Parthenogenetic: The condition in which females produce offspring without mating and, consequently, where males are seldom if ever observed.

Pedicel: A stalk.

Pedicellaria (pl. pedicellariae): Minute moveable stalked pincers that project from the skin of some echinoderms, used for grooming.

Pedicellate: Stalked.

Pelagic: Of the open sea.

Pelagosphaera larva: The dispersive stage of a sipunculid worm.

Pentacrinoid: Stalked, attached, juvenile stage of a feather star.

Pereiopod A crustacean thoracic limb composed of seven segments namely, in a sequence from the body, **coxa** (often very small and indistinct), **basis**, **ischium**, **merus**, **carpus**, **propodus** and **dactylus**. Most pereiopods are walking legs but, in some groups, one or two pairs may be **chelate**.

Pereon: The middle section of the crustacean body.

Perisarc: the chitinous exoskeleton of a hydroid.

Phylum: The largest group of seemingly related organisms: generally composed of a number of Classes.

Pilidium larva: Larva of a nematode worm (somewhat resembling an annelid trochophore).

Pinna (pl. pinnae): Side arms to cnidarian tentacles.

Plankton: Free-floating animals and plants which, whilst they may swim quite actively, are carried about by the tidal or ocean currents. (adj. planktonic).

Plate: A flat component of a molluscan or echinoderm shell.

Pleon: The abdomen of a crustacean.

Pleonite: Each of the six somites comprising the **pleon**, of a shrimp or prawn.

Pleopod: Swimming legs of crustacea. Appendages of the abdomen (pleon) in crustacea which retain the primitive biramous structure and are composed of the outer exopod and inner endopod.

Pleuron (pl. pleura): The lateral lobes of each pleonite somite in decapod crustacea.

Polyp: An 'individual' animal within a colony = zooid. (it is customary to use one word in some phyla and the other in another).

Polyramous: Multi-branched. cf. uniramous – single structure, bi-ramous – structure divided into two parts.

Proboscis: An eversible, muscular, tubular organ housed, when retracted, in the rhynchocoel; the organisation of the proboscis is of major taxonomic importance.

Proglottids: The 'repeated units' that make up the body of a cestode (tape worm) – something between a chain of zooida and the somitation of annelids.

Propus: Limb segment immediately proximal to the **dactylus**. The lateral expansion of the

propus enables a **chela** to be formed with the **dactylus**.

Protandrous: The condition whereby a sequentially hermaphroditic organism is functionally a male first, and a female later.

Protoconch: The first-formed part of a gastropod snail's shell, remaining on the apex (unless worn off) of the adult's shell. The equivalent on a bivalve shell is the **umbo**.

Protonephridia: Single-celled structures used in excretion and, possibly, with osmoregulation.

Proximal: The end nearest to the point of attachment (opposite of **distal**).

Pseudohydrotheca: A (secondary) extension of the perisarc around the base of the hydranth, in some hydroid species, forming a simple, usually frail structure perhaps not homologous with a hydrotheca but apparently similar in function.

Pseudometamerism: The serial replication of body structures, in nemerteans typically the intestinal diverticula, gonads and transverse blood vessels joining the lateral and mid-dorsal vessels, without the formation of somites; confined in nemerteans to the intestinal regions of the body.

Radial septa: In a sea anemone or coral, the partitions (septa) that subdivide the enteron lie on radii, running from near the centre to the margin.

Radial symmetry: Symmetry in which any diameter bisects the object into two essentially identical halves. In many hydromedusae, despite the cross-shaped arrangement of the radial canals the bell can be so divided along any diameter: the division does not have to be along a radial canal. Such hydromedusae are also said to have tetra-radiate symmetry. In bilateral symmetry there is only one plane about which the structure has two mirror-image halves.

Raptorial: Hunting, in the manor of a bird of prey.

Retractile: Capable of being withdrawn.

Rhabdites: Rod-like structures of uncertain function in the epidermis of some turbellarian flatworms.

Retractile: Capable of being withdrawn.

Rostrum: A beak-like structure which projects anteriorly from the front of the **carapace** in a crustacean.

Rostral Incisure: An indentation in the shell of an ostracod to accept the rostrum.

Scolex: The part of a cestode (tape worm) attached to the gut lining of its host.

Segment: In this *Key*, the word 'segment' is used for the successive sections (sometimes called articles) of an arthropod limb. The word 'somite' is used for the successive sections of the body. There is confusion of terminology in the literature.

Sessile: Without a stalk. Growing directly on the substrate.

Sensillum (pl. sensilla): A general term for a sense organ.

Seta (pl. setae): A hair or fine spine which is not innervated.

Sexual dimorphism: The condition when males and females of the same species exhibit external differences.

Shell: A non-living protective (and/or skeletal) structure secreted by an animal. Typically formed of a fibrous mesh onto which crystals of calcium carbonate have been deposited. Shells may be in one piece (univalve), in two pieces (bivalve) or be arranged in a series of plates.

Sigmoid: Strictly, 'Σ'-shaped (Greek letter sigma); generally used to mean 'S'-shaped.

Solitary: Living on its own, and not in tissue contact with other individuals (in contrast to a **colonial** animal).

Somitally: = segmentally. See **segment**.

Somitation: = segmentation. See **segment**.

Somite: A 'segment' of the body. See **segment**.

Species: A group of individual animals which, within the limitations of their breeding system, can interbreed to form fertile offspring. Members of a common gene pool. The basic unit of the classification system.

Spicule: A little spine. In sponges (Phylum Porifera), they are often the most important characters for species determination. They may be designated by size into larger **megascleres** or smaller **microscleres**; and after that by the number of axes or points they possess. Thus a **monaxon** is **monoactine** if pointed at only one end or **diactine** if pointed at both. See Hayward & Ryland (1990).

Spine: A long thin rod, probably pointed, projecting from the surface of an animal. The coarse end of the cilium-hair-bristle-spine continuum.

Statocyst: A sense organ for determining which way up an animal is – simple ones may me just a sensory cup containing a few sand grains.

Stenohaline: tolerant of only a narrow range of salinities. Usually used for truly marine animals. The opposite of euryhaline.

Sternite: The ventral plate of a body somite in an arthropod.

Stolon (adj. stolonal): A tube connecting individual members (polyps or zooids) of a dispersed colony.

Stoloniferous (of a colony): Made up of interconnecting stolons.

Strobila: The linear series of proglottids (repeated units) behind the scolex of a cestode (tape worm).

Subchela: Claw or pincer where the **dactyl** and **propus** articulate at right-angles to the long axis of the limb.

Sublittoral: Below the littoral zone. A term used for benthic organisms that are never exposed to the atmosphere = subtidal.

Sub-terminal: Not quite at the end of the body, the limb or whatever.

Subtidal: Below the tidal zone. A term used for benthic organisms that are never exposed to the atmosphere = sub-littoral.

Subtylostyle: Slightly pin-shaped monactine sponge spicules. (Tylostyles are pin-shaped).

Supralittoral: Above the littoral zone, never covered by sea water but influenced by splash and sea spray = supratidal.

Supratidal: Above the tidal zone, never covered by sea water but influenced by splash and sea spray = supralittoral.

Synanthropic: Living in association with man.

Syncitial: Without internal cell walls.

Siphon: A tube through which the animal sucks in water – **inhalant siphon** or blows it out – **exhalant siphon**.

Tagmata: The major regions of the body, head, thorax, abdomen etc.

Tantalus larva: The dispersive stage (which must be exceptional amongst crustaceans in lacking any head appendages) in the life cycle of tantulocarid crustacea.

Taxonomy: The science of classifying animals and plants.

Teloconch: Shell grown by a snail after it has settled from the plankton / or emerged from its egg capsule.

Telson: The 'tail' of a crustacean. In conjunction with the **uropods**, the telson makes up the 'tail-fan' of the animal.

Tentacles: A general term for the feelers of soft-bodied animals. Capable of movement to a variable degree, they may be used for catching food although most are sensory.

Terminal: At the end of the body, the limb or whatever.

Theca: A cup. In hydroids, an extension of the perisarc; typically surrounding and protecting one or other kind of polyp. **Hydranths** have hydrothecae, **nematophores** have nematothecae, and **gonophores** have gonothecae, etc.

Thecate: Bearing cups.

Triactines: Sponge spicules with three points. see spicules.

Tube Feet: Characteristic of echinoderms, these are the external manifestation of the water vascular system. Typically arranged in rows, **ambulacra**, they are inflated by increased pressure and deflate passively. Mainly used for locomotion.

Tubercle: A small lump.

Tunic: The skin of a sea squirt.

Tylostyles: Pin-shaped sponge spicules

Umbo (pl. umbones): The first-formed part of a bivalve shell

Uniramous: With one arm. Unlike the **biramous** limbs of crustacea, insect limbs are simple, not divided into two parts.

Uropod: The appendages of the sixth **pleonite**. They are flat and leaf-like and, with the **telson**, make up the 'tail-fan' of the animal.

Valve: The component of a shell.

Velum: A sail. Also used for the ledge around the inner margin of the bell in hydromedusae.

Ventral: Under; as in underside

Vermiform: Worm-shaped.

Vestigial: Present, but so greatly reduced in size that its usefulness must be doubtful.

Viviparous: Giving birth to live young.

Xerophilic: Living in dry habitats.

Zooid: An 'individual' animal within a colony. (= polyp; it is customary to use one word in some phyla and the other in others). Different types are distinguished by their prefixes, hence:- **Androzooid**: male, **Autozooid** or **Gastrozooid**: feeding, **Gonozooid**: brood chamber. **Gynozooid**: female, **Heterozooid**: Specialised zooid; i.e., not a feeding zooid.

Zoea: See **crustacean larvae**.

ACKNOWLEDGEMENTS

This paper had two distinct origins. The original stimulus was to complete the trio of AIDGAP keys that commenced with Croft (1986) *A Key to the Major Groups of British Freshwater Invertebrates* and continued with Tilling (1987) *A Key to the Major Groups of British Terrestrial Invertebrates*. Dr. Steve Tilling (AIDGAP Co-ordinator) has reminded me of this intention at regular intervals throughout the intervening years. I hope the result will be fit to stand in that company. The second stimulus came with the suggestion /encouragement from Dr. Doris Kermack, founding editor of the New Series, that I should write an introductory key to the *Synopses of the British Fauna* to mark publication of the 50th volume in that series.

I am, therefore, most grateful to Drs Kermack and Tilling for their vision and encouragement but, whilst they bear some responsibility for this key's existence, all the errors are mine.

SOURCES OF THE ILLUSTRATIONS

This key is a lead-in to more precise works of reference and, as far as possible, the illustrations have been copied (with permission from, we hope, the relevant authority) from the books /papers to which the reader is directed in the text. The illustrations reproduced here can be found as follows.

Pictorial Key Couplet 1
Obelia medusa. Cover illustration from Cornelius (1995)
Corystes cassivelaunus. Cover illustration from Ingle (1996)
Perinereis cultrifera Fig. 6.11A in Hayward & Ryland (1995)
Eledone cirrhosa Fig. 10.43 in Hayward & Ryland (1995)
Doto maculata Fig 57 from Thompson (1988)
Procerodes littoralis Fig. 8 from Ball & Reynoldson (1981)
Pictorial Key Couplet 2
Cornularia cornucopiae Fig. 7 from Manuel (1988)
Diadumene cincta Fig. 46 from Manuel (1988)
Sycon ciliatum Fig. 3.2 from Hayward & Ryland (1990; 1995).
Botryllus schlosseri Fig. 47a from Millar (1970)
Semibalanus balanoides Fig. 8.8 from Hayward & Ryland (1995)
Alcyonium glomeratum Fig. 10 from Manuel (1988)

Fig. 201 (Key 2:2) *Astropecten irregularis* Fig. 12.2 from Hayward & Ryland (1995).
Fig 202 [Key 2:2] *Corystes cassivelaunus.* Cover illustration from Ingle (1996)
Fig. 203 [Key 2:3] *Perinereis cultrifera* Fig. 6.11A in Hayward & Ryland (1995)
Fig. 204 [Key 2:5] *Eledone cirrhosa* Fig. 10.43 in Hayward & Ryland (1995)
Fig. 205 (Key 2:6) *Sepiola atlantica* Fig. 10.42 in Hayward & Ryland (1995)
Fig. 206 (Key 2:6) *Loligo forbesii* Fig. 10.43 in Hayward & Ryland (1995)

Fig. 207 (Key 2:8) *Trichoplax* from Pearse *et al.* (1987) p. 91
Fig. 208 (Key 2:9) *Neomenia carinata* Fig. 5A from Jones & Baxter (1987)
Fig. 209 (Key 2:9) *Chaetoderma nitidulum* Fig. 1 A, B. from Jones & Baxter (1987)
Fig. 210 [Key 2:14] *Doto maculata* Fig 57 from Thompson (1988)
Fig. 211 [Key 2:15] *Procerodes littoralis* Fig. 8 from Ball & Reynoldson (1981)
Fig. 212 (Key 2:15) *Leptoplana tremellaris* cover illustration from Prudhoe (1982)
Fig. 213 (Key 2:17) *Onchidella celtica* from Hayward *et al.* (1996)
Fig. 214 (Key 2:17) *Archidoris pseudoargus*. Fig. 95a from Thompson (1988)

Fig. 301 (Key 3:4) *Pomatoceros* sp. tubes plate IV from Barrett & Yonge (1958)
Fig. 302 [Key 3:5] *Sabella* tube from Hayward *et al.* (1996)
Fig. 303 [Key 3:5] *Lanice conchilega* and
Fig. 304 [Key 3:5] *Sabellaria* tubes plate V from Barrett & Yonge (1958)
Fig. 305 (Key 3:8) *Cliona intestinalis* cover illustration from Millar (1970)
Fig. 306 (Key 3:8) *Sycon ciliatum* Fig. 3.2 from Hayward & Ryland (1990; 1995)
Fig. 307 (Key 3:9) *Botryllus schlosseri* Fig. 47a from Millar (1970)
Fig. 308 (Key 3:9) *Halichondria panicea*. Fig. 3.5 from Hayward & Ryland (1995)

Fig. 401 (Key 4:4) *Astropecten irregularis* Fig. 12.2 from Hayward & Ryland (1995)

Fig. 402 (Key 4:5) *Crossaster papposus* (Fig. 12.3 from Hayward & Ryland (1995)

Fig. 403 (Key 4:5) pedicellaria from Pearse *et al.* (1987)

Fig. 404 (Key 4:5) *Asterias rubens* Fig. 15.5 from Hayward & Ryland (1990)

Fig. 405 (Key 4:6) *Antedon bifida* Fig. 12.2 from Hayward & Ryland (1995)

Fig. 406 (Key 4:7) *Gorgonocephalus caputmedusae* (as *Astrophyton scutatum*) from Forbes (1861) p. 67

Fig. 407 (Key 4:7) *Ophiura texturata* from Forbes (1861) p. 22

Fig. 408 (Key 4:10) *Echinus esculentus* (as *E. sphaera*) from Forbes (1861) p. 149

Fig. 409 (Key 4:11) *Echinocyamus pusillus*. Fig. 12.8 from Hayward & Ryland (1995)

Fig. 410 (Key 4:11) *Spatangus purpureus* from Forbes (1861) p. 182.

Fig. 411 (Key 4:12) *Leptosynapta inhaerens* Fig. 12.10 from Hayward & Ryland (1995).

Fig. 412 (Key 4:12) *Cucumaria communis* from Forbes (1861) p. 217

Fig. 413 (Key 4:13) *Holothuria forskali* Fig. 15,12 from Hayward & Ryland (1990; 1995)

Fig. 414 (Key 4:13) *Cucumaria frondosa* Fig. 15,12 from Hayward & Ryland (1990; 1995)

Fig. 415 (Key 4:15) *Cornularia cornucopiae* Fig. 7 from Manuel (1988)

Fig. 416 (Key 4:15) *Diadumene cincta* Fig. 46 from Manuel (1988)

Fig. 417 (Key 4:17) *Eunicella verrucosa* Fig. 13 from Manuel (1988)

Fig. 418 (Key 4:17) *Virgularia mirabilis* Fig. 15 from Manuel (1988)

Fig. 419 (Key 4:18) *Sarcodictyon roseum* Fig. 8 from Manuel (1988)

Fig. 420 (Key 4:18) *Alcyonium glomeratum* Fig. 10 from Manuel (1988)

Fig. 421 (Key 4:19) nematocysts from Pearse *et al.* (1987) p.108

Fig. 422 (Key 4:21) *Laomedea flexuosa* Fig. 65B from Cornelius (1995a).

Fig. 423 (Key 4:21) *Hydractinia echinata* from Crothers & Crothers (1983)

Fig. 424 (Key 4:22) *Sertularia argentea* Fig. 20d from Cornelius (1995b)

Fig. 425 (Key 4:22) *Calycella syringa* Fig. 42c from Cornelius (1995a)

Fig. 426 (Key 4:23) *Laomedea flexuosa* Fig. 65b from Cornelius (1995b)

Fig. 427 (Key 4:23) *Lafoea dumosa* Fig. 60D from Cornelius (1995a)

Fig. 428 (Key 4:24) *Halecium beanii* Fig, 62c from Cornelius (1995a)

Fig. 429 (Key 4:24) *Bougainvillia fruticosa* Fig. 19a from Cornelius (1995a)

Fig. 430 (Key 4:25) *Parazoanthus anguicomus* Fig. 28 from Manuel (1988)

Fig. 431 (Key 4:26) *Corynactis viridis* Fig. 76 from Manuel (1988)

Fig. 432 (Key 4:26) *Lophelia pertusa* Fig. 80 from Manuel (1988)

Fig. 433 (Key 4:27) *Pedicellina cernua* Fig. 46 from Nielsen (1989)

Fig. 434 (Key 4:28) *Alcyonidium mammillatum* Fig. 13A from Hayward (1985)

Fig. 435 (Key 4:29) *Crisia ramosa* Fig. 15 from Hayward & Ryland (1985)

Fig. 436 (Key 4:29) *Electra pilosa* Fig. 22 from Ryland & Hayward (1977)

Fig. 437 (Key 4:30) *Haliclystus auricula* Fig. 4.2 from Hayward & Ryland (1990; 1995)

Fig. 438 (Key 4:33) *Halommohydra octopodides* Fig. 18 from Cornelius (1995a)

Fig. 439 (Key 4:34) *Pachycerianthus multiplicatus* Fig. 21 from Manuel (1988).

Fig. 440 (Key 4:34) *Halcampa chrysanthellum* Fig. 68 from Manuel (1988).

Fig. 441 (Key 4:35) *Caryophyllia smithii* Fig. 78 from Manuel (1988)

Fig. 442 (Key 4:36) *Corynactis viridis* Fig. 76 from Manuel (1988)

Fig. 443 (Key 4:36) *Actinia equina* Fig. 33 from Manuel (1988)

Fig. 444 (Key 4:38) *Cerianthus lloydi* Fig. 20 from Manuel (1988)

Fig. 445 (Key 4:39) *Velella velella* Fig. 61B from Kirkpatrick & Pugh (1984)

Fig. 446 (Key 4:39) *Physalia physalis* Fig. 5 from Kirkpatrick & Pugh (1984)

Fig. 447 (Key 4:40) *Nanomia cara* Fig. 4A from Kirkpatrick & Pugh (1984)

Fig. 448 (Key 4:42) *Beroe cucumis* from Greve (1975)

Fig. 449 (Key 4:43) *Mertensia ovum* from Greve (1975)

Fig. 450 (Key 4:43) *Bolinopsis infundibulum* from Greve (1975)

Fig. 451 (Key 4:45) *Aeginura grimaldii* Fig. 16 from Cornelius (1995a)

Fig. 452 (Key 4:46) *Phialella quadrata*. Fig. 39A from Cornelius (1995a)

Fig. 453 (Key 4:46) *Euphysa aurata* Fig. 19 right from Cornelius (1995a)

Fig. 454 (Key 4:47) *Aglantha digitale* Fig. 17 from Cornelius (1995a)

Fig. 455 (Key 4:47) *Cosmetira pilosella* Fig. 28a from Cornelius (1995a)

Fig. 456 (Key 4:48) *Craspedacusta sowerbii* Fig. 14 from Cornelius (1995a)

Fig. 457 (Key 4:48) *Euphysa aurata* Fig. 19b from Cornelius (1995a)

Fig. 458 (Key 4:49) *Rhizostoma octopus* from Russell (1978)

Fig. 459 (Key 4:50) *Nausithoe globifera* Fig. 14 from Russell (1976)

Fig. 460 (Key 4:50) *Chrysaora hysoscella* plate from Russell (1978)

Fig. 501 (Key 5:3) *Tripetesa lampas* Fig. 16 from Bassindale (1960)

Fig. 502 *Carcinus maenas.* Fig. 1 from Crothers (1967)

Fig. 503 (Key 5:4) *Semibalanus balanoides* Fig. 8.8 from Hayward & Ryland (1995)

Fig. 504 (Key 5:4) *Lepas pectinata* Fig 8.8 from Hayward & Ryland (1995)

Fig. 505 (Key 5:8) *Conchoderma* sp. Fig. 8.7 from Hayward & Ryland (1995)

Fig. 506 (Key 5:9) *Cyamus globicipitis* Fig. 13 from Harrison (1943)

Fig. 507 (Key 5:9) *Balaenophilus unisetus* Fig. 53L from Gotto (1993)

Fig. 508 (Key 5:10) *Paragnathia formica* praniza larva Fig. 4 from Naylor (1972)

Fig. 509 (Key 5:10) *Caligus minima* Fig. 13 from Kabata (1993)

Fig. 510 (Key 5:12) *Athelges paguri* Fig. 23D from Naylor (1972)

Fig. 511 (Key 5:12) *Modiolicola insignis* Fig. 17a from Gotto (1993)

Fig. 512 (Key 5:13) *Acasta spongites* Fig. 8.9 from Hayward & Ryland (1995)

Fig. 513 (Key 5:13) *Sacculina carcini* Fig. 8.11 from Hayward & Ryland (1990; 1995)

Fig. 514 (Key 5:17) *Nebalia bipes* Fig. 27a from Mauchline (1984)

Fig. 515 (Key 5:18) *Verruca stroemia* cypris from Bassindale (1960)

Fig. 516 (Key 5:19) *Cytherella abyssorum* Fig. 21D from Athersutch *et al.* (1989)

Fig. 517 (Key 5:20) cover illustration from Angel (1993)

Fig. 518 (Key 5:20) *Cythere lutea* Fig. 21E from Athersutch *et al.* (1989)

Fig. 519 (Key 5:22) *Pagurus bernhardus* Fig 10 from Crothers & Crothers (1988).

Fig. 520 (Key 5:22) *Macropipus tuberculatus* Fig. 22 from Crothers & Crothers (1988).

Fig. 521 (Key 5:23) *Thysanoessa inermis* cover illustration from Mauchline (1984)

Fig. 522 (Key 5:23) *Palaemon elegans* Fig 9 from Smaldon (1979)

Fig. 523 (Key 5:23) *Axius stirhynchus* cover illustration from Boyden *et al.* (1984).

Fig. 524 (Key 5:24) female and praniza larva of *Paragnathia formica* Fig 4B, 4C from Naylor (1972)

Fig. 525 (Key 5:26) *Parasinelobus chevreuxi* cover illustration from Holdich & Jones (1983)

Fig. 526 (Key 5:26) *Diastylis rathkei* cover illustration from Jones (1976)

Fig. 527 (Key 5:27) *Meiosquilla desmaresti* Fig. 21a from Mauchline (1984)

Fig. 528 , 529 (Key 5:27) *Mesopodopsis slabberi* Fig. 8.19E Hayward & Ryland (1995)

Fig. 530 (Key 5:29) *Calanoida* in Fig 4.3.2 from Huys & Boxshall (1991)

Fig. 531 (Key 5:30) *Idotea granulosa* cover illustration from Naylor (1972)

Fig. 532 (Key 5:30) *Calliopus laeviusculus* Fig,. 8.28 Hayward & Ryland (1995)

Fig. 533 (Key 5:32) millipede Fig. 1a from Blower (1985)

Fig. 534 (Key 5:32) a marine centipede from Pearse *et al.* (1987)

Fig. 535 (Key 5:34) A typical fly. Fig. 1 from Tilling (1987)

Fig. 536 (Key 5:35) *Petrobius maritima* Fig. 9.4 from Hayward & Ryland (1995)

Fig. 537(Key 5:36) *Anurida maritima* Fig. 9.4 from Hayward & Ryland (1995)

Fig. 538 (Key 5:36) A beetle larva from Tilling (1987) p. 729

Fig. 539 (Key 5:37) *Neobisium maritimum* Fig. 15A from Legg & Jones (1988)

Fig. 540 (Key 5:38) spider from Tilling (1976) p. 715

Fig. 541 (Key 5:39) *Agauopsis brevipalpus* cover illustration from Green & Macquitty (1987)

Fig. 542 (Key 5:39) *Pycnogonum littorale* cover illustration from King (1974)

Fig. 601 (Key 6:3) *Sepia officinalis* Fig 1a from Muus (1963)

Fig. 602 (Key 6:3) *Loligo vulgaris* from Muus (1963)

Fig. 603 (Key 6:5) *Lamellaria perspicua* p. 199 from Hayward *et al.* (1996)

Fig. 604 (Key 6:5) *Colpodaspis pusilla* Fig. 6B from Thompson (1988)

Fig. 605 (Key 6:6) *Philine aperta* Fig. 18c from Thompson (1988)

Fig. 606 (Key 6:7) *Aplysia depilans* Fig. 28A from Thompson (1988)

Fig. 607 (Key 6:7) *Berthella plumula* Fig. 30A from Thompson (1988)

Fig. 608 (Key 6:10) *Caecum glabrum* Fig. 117 from Graham (1988)

Fig. 609 (Key 6:11) a dentalioid scaphopod Fig. 24 from Jones & Baxter (1987)

Fig. 610 (Key 6:11) *Pulsellum lofotense* Fig. 26 from Jones & Baxter (1987)

Fig. 611 (Key 6:13) *Pelseneeria stylifera* Fig. 232 from Graham (1988)

Fig. 612 (Key 6:14) *Acteon tornatilis* Fig. 4 from Thompson (1988)

Fig. 613 (Key 6:15) *Gibbula umbilicalis* Fig. 31b from Graham (1988)

Fig. 614 (Key 6:16) *Littorina littorea* Fig. 60 from Graham (1988)

Fig. 615 (Key 6:17) *Nucella lapillus* Fig. 150 from Graham (1988)

Fig. 616 (Key 6:17) *Aporrhais pespelecani* Fig. 120 from Graham (1988)

Fig. 617 (Key 6:20) *Akera bullata* Fig. 1D from Thompson (1988)

Fig. 618 (Key 6:20) *Diaphana minuta* Fig. 5b from Thompson (1988)

Fig. 619 (Key 6:21) *Otina ovata* p. 231 from of Hayward *et al.* (1996)

Fig. 620 (Key 6:22) *Haliotis tuberculata* Fig. 14 from Graham (1988)

Fig. 621 (Key 6:23) *Crepidula fornicata* Fig. 126A from Graham (1988)

Fig. 622 (Key 6:24) *Patella vulgata* Fig. 20 from Graham (1988)

Fig. 623 (Key 6:24) *Trivia monacha* Fig. 132 from Graham (1988)

Fig. 624 (Key 6:27) *Acanthochitona fascicularis* Fig. 22A from Jones & Baxter (1987)

Fig. 625 (Key 6:28) a generalised chiton Fig. 11c from Jones & Baxter (1987)

Fig. 626 (Key 6:29) *Tripetesa lampas* Fig. 16 from Bassindale (1960)

Fig. 627 (Key 6:30) *Semibalanus balanoides* Fig. 8.8 from Hayward & Ryland (1995)

Fig. 628 (Key 6:30) *Lepas pectinata* Fig 8.8 from Hayward & Ryland (1995)

Fig. 629 (Key 6:33) *Crania anomala* Fig. 11 from Howard *et al.*, (1979)

Fig. 630 (Key 6:33) *Ostrea edulis* Fig. 4a from Tebble (1966)

Fig. 631 (Key 6:35) *Hemithiris psittacea* Fig. 14a from Howard *et al.*, (1979)

Fig. 632 (Key 6:35) *Terebratulina retusa* Fig. 17 from Howard *et al.*, (1979)

Fig. 633 (Key 6:36) *Heteranomia squamula* Fig 4b from Tebble (1966)

Fig. 634 (Key 6:38) *Pinna fragilis* Fig. 25 from Tebble (1966)

Fig. 635 (Key 6:38) *Modiolus barbatus* Fig. 21 from Tebble (1966)

Fig. 636 (Key 6:39) *Lasaea adansoni* Fig. 13A from Tebble (1966) (as *L. rubra*)

Fig. 637 (Key 6:40) *Sphenia binghami* Fig. 90 from Tebble (1966)

Fig. 638 (Key 6:41) *Venerupis pullastra* Fig. 58 from Tebble (1966)

Fig. 639 (Key 6:42) *Lima subauriculata* Fig. 28 from Tebble (1966)

Fig. 640 (Key 6:42) *Galeomma turtoni* Fig. 36 from Tebble (1966)

Fig. 641 (Key 6:44) *Nucula turgida* Fig. 1 from Tebble (1966)

Fig. 642 (Key 6:44) *Limopsis aurita* Fig. 17 from Tebble (1966)

Fig. 643 (Key 6:45) *Chlamys nivea* Fig. 3 from Tebble (1966)

Fig. 644 (Key 6:46) *Cuspidaria costellata* Fig. 110a from Tebble (1966)

Fig. 645 (Key 6:47) *Pholas dactylus* Fig. 94 from Tebble (1966)

Fig. 646 (Key 6:50) *Crenella prideauxi* Fig. 23 from Tebble (1966)

Fig. 647 (Key 6:50) *Devonia perrieri* Fig. 36c from Tebble (1966)

Fig. 648 (Key 6:51) *Thyasira croulinsis* Fig. 34 from Tebble (1966)

Fig. 649 (Key 6:52) *Modiolus barbatus* Fig. 21 from Tebble (1966)

Fig. 650 (Key 6:53) *Pinna fragilis* Fig. 25 from Tebble (1966)

Fig. 651 (Key 6:53) *Gastrochaena dubia* from Hayward & Ryland (1990; 1995) p.781

Fig. 652 (Key 6:54) *Pandora albida* Fig. 106 from Tebble (1966)

Fig. 653 (Key 6:55) *Scrobicularia plana* Fig. 10 from Tebble (1966)

Fig. 654 (Key 6:55) *Cyprina islandica* Fig. 45 as Arctica from Tebble (1966)

Fig. 655 (Key 6:57) *Solen marginatus* Fig. 86 from Tebble (1966)

Fig. 656 (Key 6:58) *Panomya arctica* Fig. 92 from Tebble (1966)

Fig. 657 (Key 6:58) *Venerupis decussata* Fig. 59 from Tebble (1966)

Fig. 658 (Key 6:59) *Corbula gibba* Fig. 91 from Tebble (1966)

Fig. 659 (Key 6:61) *Poromya granulata* Fig. 107 from Tebble (1966)

Fig. 660 (Key 6:61) *Mactra corallina* Fig. 66 from Tebble (1966)

Fig. 661 (Key 6:62) *Mya arenaria* Fig. 89 from Tebble (1966)

Fig. 662 (Key 6:62) *Thracia pubescens* Fig. 104 from Tebble (1966)

Fig. 701 (Key 7:2) *Myzostoma cirriferum* Fig. 152h from Fauvel (1927)

Fig. 702 (Key 7:2) *Spinther arcticus* Fig. 13A from George & Hartmann-Schröder (1985)

Fig. 703 (Key 7:4) larva of a chironomid midge. Key 7 Fig 7 from Croft (1986)

Fig. 704 (Key 7:5) *Priapulus caudatus* Fig. 7.1 from Hayward & Ryland (1990; 1995)

Fig. 705 (Key 7:6) *Brumptiana lineata* Fig. 6.30 from Hayward & Ryland (1990; 1995)

Fig. 706 (Key 7:7) Naidid worm. Fig. 6.27 from Hayward & Ryland (1995)

Fig. 707 (Key 7:11) *Flabelligera affinis* from Hayward *et al.* (1996)

Fig. 708 (Key 7:11) *Pectinaria* from Hayward *et al.* (1996)

Fig. 709 (Key 7:12) *Euphrosyne foliosa*. page 91 of Hayward *et al.* (1996)

Fig. 710 (Key 7:13) *Lepidonotus clava*. Fig. 6.4A from Hayward & Ryland (1995)

Fig. 711 (Key 7:14) *Typosyllis prolifera*. Fig. 6.16A from Hayward & Ryland (1995)

Fig. 712 (Key 7:15) *Tomopteris helgolandica* Fig. 57A from Pleijel & Dales (1991)

Fig. 713 (Key 7:16) *Platynereis dumerili* Fig. 6.11E from Hayward & Ryland (1995)

Fig. 714 (Key 7:16) *Lumbrineris latreilli* Fig. p. 99 from Hayward, Nelson-Smith & Shields (1996)

Fig. 715 (Key 7:19) *Pomatoceros lamarkii* Plate IV from Barrett & Yonge (1958) as *P. triqueter*

Fig. 716 (Key 7:18) *Sabellaria* tubes. Plate V from Barrett & Yonge (1958)

Fig. 717 (Key 7:19) *Polydora ciliata* Fig. p. 101 from Hayward, Nelson-Smith & Shields (1996)

Fig. 718 (Key 7:20) *Arenicola marina* Fig. 6.3K from Hayward & Ryland (1995)

Fig. 719 (Key 7:21) *Cirratulus cirratus* Fig. 6.5C from Hayward & Ryland (1995)

Fig. 720 (Key 7:22) *Polydora ciliata* Fig. 6.15A from Hayward & Ryland (1995)

Fig. 721 (Key 7:23) *Amphitrite figulus* Fig. 6.17 from Hayward & Ryland (1990; 1995)

Fig. 722 (Key 7:23) head of a sabellid from the key by Dr. J. D. George in, for example, George & Hartmann-Schröder (1985)

Fig. 723 (Key 7:25) *Procerodes littoralis* Fig. 8 from Ball & Reynoldson (1981)

Fig. 724 (Key 7:25) *Leptoplana tremellaris* cover illustration from Prudhoe (1982)

Fig. 725 (Key 7:26) *Priapulus caudatus* Plate 11 from Barrett & Yonge (1958)

Fig. 726 (Key 7:27) *Sagitta elegans* Fig. 10 from Pierrot-Bults & Chidgey (1988)

Fig. 727 (Key 7:28) detached tentacles from Fig. 6.17 from Hayward & Ryland (1990; 1995)

Fig. 728 (Key 7:29) *Catanema macintyrei* Fig. 166 from Platt & Warwick (1988)

Fig. 729 (Key 7:31) *Phoronis muelleri* Fig. 14 from Emig (1979)

Fig. 730 (Key 7:33) *Siboglinum* sp. Fig. 7.1 from Hayward & Ryland (1990; 1995)

Fig. 731 (Key 7:35) *Leptosynapta inhaerens* Fig. 15,14 from Hayward & Ryland (1990; 1995)

Fig. 732 (Key 7:36) *Holothuria forskali* Fig. 15,12 from Hayward & Ryland (1990; 1995)

Fig. 733 (Key 7:36) *Cucumaria frondosa* Fig. 15,12 from Hayward & Ryland (1990; 1995)

Fig. 734 (Key 7:37) *Pachycerianthus multiplicatus* Fig. 21 from Manuel (1988)

Fig. 735 (Key 7:37) *Halcampa chrysanthellum* Fig. 68 from Manuel (1988)

Fig. 736 (Key 7:39) *Neomenia carinata* Fig. 5A from Jones & Baxter (1987)

Fig. 737 (Key 7:39) *Chaetoderma nitidulum* Fig. 3A from Jones & Baxter (1987)

Fig. 738 (Key 7:40) *Saccoglossus ruber* Fig. 16.1 from Hayward & Ryland (1990; 1995)

Fig. 739 (Key 7:41) *Emplectonema neesi* Fig. 36 from Gibson (1982)

Fig. 740 (Key 7:42) *Bonellia viridis* Fig. 7.1 from Hayward & Ryland (1990; 1995)

Fig. 741 (Key 7:42) *Golfingia vulgaris* Fig. 36 from Gibbs(1977)

REFERENCES

ACKERS, R. Graham, MOSS, David, PICTON, Bernard E., and STONE, Shirley E., (1985). *Sponges of the British Isles - a Colour Guide and Working Document*. Marine Conservation Society. Ross-on-Wye.

ALLEN, J. A., (1967). *The Fauna of the Clyde Sea Area. Crustacea: Euphausiacea and Decapoda*. Scottish Marine Biological Association, Millport.

ANDERSON, D. T., (1973). *Embryology and Phylogeny of Annelids and Arthropods*. Pergamon. Oxford.

ANDERSON, D. T., (1994). *Barnacles. Structure, function, development and evolution*. Chapman and Hall, London.

ANGEL, Martin V., (1993). *Marine planktonic Ostracods*. Synopses of the British Fauna (New Series) No. 48, Field Studies Council, Shrewsbury.

ATHERSUCH, J., HORNE, D. J. and WHITTAKER, J. E., (1989). *Marine and brackish-water Ostracods (Superfamilies Cypridacea and Cytheracea)*. Synopses of the British Fauna (New Series) No. 43, E. J. Brill, Leiden.

BALL, Ian R., and REYNOLDSON, T. B., (1981). *British Planarians*. Synopses of the British Fauna (New Series) No. 19 Cambridge University Press.

BARNES, R. S. K., (1984). *A Synoptic Classification of Living Organisms*. Blackwell Scientific Publications, Oxford.

BARNES, R. S. K., CALOW, P. and OLIVE, P. J. W., (1988). *The Invertebrates: a new synthesis*. Blackwell Scientific Publications, Oxford.

BARRETT, John H., and YONGE, C. M., (1958). *Collins Pocket Guide to the Seashore*. Collins, London.

BASSINDALE, R., (1960). *British Barnacles*. Synopses of the British Fauna No. 14 Linnean Society of London.

BERRILL, N. J., (1950). *The Tunicata, with an account of the British species.* Ray Society. London.
BERZINS, Bruno, (1960). Rotatoria *Fiches d'identification du zooplancton*, **84-89**. Conseil International pour l'Exploration de la Mer. Andr. Fred. Høst and Fils, Copenhagen.
BLOWER, J. Gordon, (1985). *Millipedes* Synopses of the British Fauna (New Series) No. 35 E. J. Brill/Dr. W. Backhuys. Leiden.
BOADEN, P. J. S., (1963). Marine Gastrotricha from the interstitial fauna of some North Wales beaches. *Proceedings of the Zoological Society of London*, **140**, 485-502.
BOURDON, R., 1965. Inventaire de la faune marine de Roscoff: Décapodes-Stomatopodes. *Travaux de la Station Biologique de Roscoff*, **16**, 1-45.
BOXSHALL, G. A. and LINCOLN, R. J., (1987). The life cycle of the Tantulocarida (Crustacea). *Philosophical Transactions of the Royal Society of London, Series B*, **315**, 267-303.
BOYDEN, C. R., CROTHERS, J. H., LITTLE, C. and METTAM, C., (1977). The intertidal invertebrate fauna of the Severn Estuary. *Field Studies*, **4**, 477-554
BRINKHURST, R. O., (1982). *British and Other Marine and Estuarine Oligochaetes.* Synopses of the British Fauna (New Series) No. 21 Cambridge University Press.
BRUCE, J. R., COLMAN, J. S. and JONES, N. S., (1963). *Marine Fauna of the Isle of Man, and its surrounding seas.* Liverpool University Press.
CAMERON, R. A. D. (1994). *Keys to Land Snails.* AIDGAP Test Version of the keys prepared for the Synopses of the British Fauna (New Series) No. 6 (2nd Edition). Field Studies Council, Shrewsbury.
CAUDWELL, C. M., JONES, A. M. and KILLEEN, I. J., (1995). Three Solenogastres from the Irish Sea, new to the British Marine Area, *Journal of Conchology*, **35**, 257-269.
CHAMBERS S. J. and MUIR, R. I., (1997). *Polychaetes: British Chrysopetaloidea, Pisionoidea and Aphroditoidea.* Synopses of the British Fauna (New Series) No. 54. Field Studies Council, Shrewsbury.
CHENG, Lanna, (1976). *Marine Insects.* North Holland / American Elsevier.
CHRISTIANSEN, Marit E., (1969). *Decapoda Brachyura. Marine Invertebrates of Scandinavia 2.* Scandinavian University Books, Universitets Forlaget, Oslo.
CLARK, Paul F., (1985). *North East Atlantic Crabs - an atlas of distribution.* Marine Conservation Society, Ross-on-Wye.
CLARK, R. B., (1960). *The Fauna of the Clyde Sea Area, Polychaeta.* Scottish Marine Biological Association, Millport.
CORNELIUS, P. F. S., (1995). *North-West European Thecate Hydroids and their Medusae.* Synopses of the British Fauna (New Series) No. 50, Part 1. 344 pages. Part 2. 384 pages. Field Studies Council, Shrewsbury.
CROFT, P. S., (1986). A Key to the Major Groups of British Freshwater Invertebrates. *Field Studies*, **6**, 531-579.
CROMPTON, D. W. T., (1970). *An ecological approach to acanthocephalan physiology.* Cambridge Monographs on Experimental Biology, 17. Cambridge University Press.
CROTHERS, J. H., (1967). The biology of the shore crab *Carcinus maenas* (L.) 1. The background - anatomy, growth and life history. *Field Studies*, **2**, 407-434.
CROTHERS, John and CROTHERS, Marilyn, (1983: 1988). A key to the Crabs and Crab-like Animals of British Inshore Waters. *Field Studies*, **5**, 753-806.
DAHL, E., (1985). Crustacea Leptostraca, principles of taxonomy and a revision of European shelf species. *Sarsia*, **70**, 135-165.
DALES, R. P., (1957). Heteropoda Families: Atlantidae, Carinariidae and Pterotracheidae. *Fiches d'identification du zooplancton*, **66**, Conseil International pour l'Exploration de la Mer. Andr. Fred. Høst and Fils, Copenhagen.
DANCE, S. Peter (ed) (1974). *The Encyclopaedia of Shells.* Blandford Press. Poole.
DANTANT, L. and LUQUE, A., (1994). Cocculiniformia and Lepetidae (Gastropoda: Archaeogastropoda) from Iberian Waters. *Journal of Molluscan Studies*, **60**, 277-313.
DELANEY, M. J., (1954). Thysanura and Diplura. *Handbooks for the Identification of British Insects. Vol. 1 Part 2.* Royal Entomological Society. London.
DELLA CROCE, N., (1974). Cladocera. *Fiches d'identification du zooplancton*, Sheet **143**. Conseil International pour l'Exploration de la Mer.
DOBSON, Terry, (1976). *Seaweed Flies (Diptera; Coelopidae etc.)* Chapter 16 of CHENG, Lanna, (1976). *Marine Insects.* North Holland / American Elsevier.
DOYEN, John T., (1976). *Marine Beetles (Coleoptera excluding Staphylinidae)* in CHENG, Lanna, *Marine Insects.* North Holland / American Elsevier.
DUNBAR, M. J., (1963). Amphipoda Sub-Order: Hyperiidea. Family Hyperiidae *Fiches d'identification du zooplancton*, **103**. Conseil International pour l'Exploration de la Mer. Andr. Fred. Høst and Fils, Copenhagen.

EMIG, C. C., (1979). *British and Other Phoronids*. Synopses of the British Fauna (New Series) No. 13 Academic Press. London.

FAUVEL, P. (1927). *Polychetès sedéntaires*. Faune de France, 16, Paris.

FINCHAM, A. A. and WILLIAMSON, D. I., (1978). Crustacea Decapoda larvae VI. Caridea families Palaemonidae and Processidae. *Fiches d'identification du zooplancton*, **159/160**. Conseil International pour l'Exploration de la Mer. Andr. Fred. Høst and Fils, Copenhagen.

FORBES, Edward, (1861). *A History of British Starfishes and other animals of the class Echinodermata*. Van Voorst, London.

FOSTER, W. A. and TREHERNE, J. E., (1976). *Insects of marine saltmarshes: problems and adaptations*. Chapter 2 of CHENG, Lanna, (1976). *Marine Insects*. North Holland / American Elsevier.

FRASER, J. H., (1981). *British Pelagic Tunicates*. Synopses of the British Fauna (New Series) No. 20, Cambridge University Press.

FRETTER, V. and GRAHAM, A., (1962). *British Prosobranch Molluscs*. Ray Society. London. 755pp.

FRETTER, V. and GRAHAM, A., (1976). The Prosobranch Molluscs of Britain and Denmark Part 1 - Pleurotomariacea, Fissurellacea and Patellacea. *Journal of Molluscan Studies* Supplement No. 1

FRETTER, V. and GRAHAM, A., (1977). The Prosobranch Molluscs of Britain and Denmark Part 2 - Trochacea. *Journal of Molluscan Studies* Supplement No. 3

FRETTER, V. and GRAHAM, A., (1978a). The Prosobranch Molluscs of Britain and Denmark Part 3 - Neritacea, Viviparacea, Valvatacea, Terrestrial and Freshwater Littorinacea and Rissoacea. *Journal of Molluscan Studies* Supplement No. 5

FRETTER, V. and GRAHAM, A., (1978b). The Prosobranch Molluscs of Britain and Denmark Part 4 - Marine Rissoacea. *Journal of Molluscan Studies* Supplement No. 6

FRETTER, V. and GRAHAM, A., (1980). The Prosobranch Molluscs of Britain and Denmark Part 5 - Marine Littorinacea. *Journal of Molluscan Studies* Supplement No. 7

FRETTER, V. and GRAHAM, A., (1981). The Prosobranch Molluscs of Britain and Denmark Part 6 - Cerithiacea, Strombacea, Hipponicacea, Calyptraecea, Lamellariacea, Cypraecea, Naticacea, Tonnacea, Heteropoda. *Journal of Molluscan Studies* Supplement No. 9

FRETTER, V. and GRAHAM, A., (1982). The Prosobranch Molluscs of Britain and Denmark Part 7 - 'Heterogastropoda' (Cerithiopsacea, Triforacea, Epitoniacea, Eulimacea). *Journal of Molluscan Studies* Supplement No. 11.

FRETTER, V. and GRAHAM, A., (1985). The Prosobranch Molluscs of Britain and Denmark Part 8 - Neogastropoda. *Journal of Molluscan Studies* Supplement No. 15

FRETTER, V. and GRAHAM, A., (1986). The Prosobranch Molluscs of Britain and Denmark Part 9 - Pyramidellacea. *Journal of Molluscan Studies* Supplement No. 16

FRETTER, Vera. and GRAHAM, Alastair., (1994). *British Prosobranch Molluscs: their functional anatomy and ecology*. Ray Society. London. 820pp.

FUNCH, Peter and KRISTENSEN, Reinhardt Mobjerg, (1995). Cycliophora is a new phylum with affinities to Entoprocta and Ectoprocta. *Nature, London*, **378**, 711-714.

GARWOOD, P. R., (1981). Polychaeta - Errantia. Marine Fauna of the Cullercoats District, No. 9. *Report of the Dove Marine Laboratory (Third Series)*, **22**, 192pp.

GARWOOD, P. R., (1982). Polychaeta - Sedentaria including Archiannelida. Marine Fauna of the Cullercoats District, No. 10. *Report of the Dove Marine Laboratory (Third Series)*, **23**, 273pp.

GEORGE, J. D. and HARTMANN-SCHRÖDER, G., (1977). *Polychaetes: British Amphinomida, Spintherida and Eunicida*. Synopses of the British Fauna (New Series) No. 32 E. J. Brill/ Dr. W. Backhuys. Leiden.

GIBBS, P. E., (1977). *British Sipunculans*. Synopses of the British Fauna (New Series) No. 12 Academic Press.

GIBSON, Ray, (1982). *British Nemerteans*. Synopses of the British Fauna (New Series) No. 24. Cambridge University Press.

GIBSON, Ray, (1994). *Nemerteans*. Synopses of the British Fauna (New Series) No. 24. Second Edition. Field Studies Council, Shrewsbury.

GOTTO, V., (1993). *Commensal and Parasitic Copepods associated with Marine Invertebrates (and whales)*. Synopses of the British Fauna (New Series) No. 46. Universal Book Services / Dr. W. Backhuys. Oegstgeest.

GRAHAM, Alastair, (1988). *Molluscs: Prosobranch and Pyramidellid Gastropods*. Synopses of the British Fauna (New Series) No. 2 (Second Edition) E. J. Brill / Dr. W. Backhuys. Leiden.

GREEN, J., and MACQUITTY, Miranda, (1987). *Halacarid Mites*. Synopses of the British Fauna (New Series) No. 36 E. J. Brill / Dr. W. Backhuys. Leiden.

GREVE, W., (1975). Ctenophora. *Fiches d'identification du zooplancton*, **146**. Conseil International pour l'Exploration de la Mer. Andr. Fred. Høst and Fils, Copenhagen.

HARRISON, R. J., (1943). *Caprellidea (Amphipoda Crustacea)*. Synopses of the British Fauna No. 2. The Linnean Society of London.

HARTOG, C. den, (1974). *Saltmarsh Turbellaria* in RISER, Nathan W., and MORSE, M. Patricia, *Biology of the Turbellaria*. McGraw Hill.

HASHIMOTO, Hiroshi, (1976). *Non-biting midges of marine habitats (Diptera, Chironomidae)*. Chapter 14 of CHENG, Lanna, (1976). *Marine Insects*. North Holland / American Elsevier.

HASZPRUNAR, Gerhard, (1988). A preliminary phylogenetic analysis of the streptoneurous gastropods. *Malacological Review*, Supplement 4, 7-16.

HAYWARD, P. J., NELSON-SMITH, A. and SHIELDS. C., (1996). *Collins Pocket Guide. Sea Shore of Britain and Northern Europe*. HarperCollins.

HAYWARD, P. J. and RYLAND, J. S., (1990). *The Marine Fauna of the British Isles and North-West Europe*. Clarendon Press, Oxford. 2 Volumes.

HAYWARD, P. J. and RYLAND, J. S., (1995). *Handbook of the Marine Fauna of North-West Europe*. Oxford University Press.

HELLER, J., (1993). Hermaphroditism in molluscs. *Biological Journal of the Linnean Society*, **48**, 19-42.

HEIP, C., VINCX, M., SMOL, N. and VRANKEN, G., 1982. The systematics and ecology of free-living marine nematodes. *Helminthological Abstracts* (Series B), **51**, 1-31.

HEIP, C., VINCX, M. and VRANKEN, G., 1985. The ecology of marine nematodes. *Oceanography and Marine Biology. An annual review*, **23**, 399-489.

HICKMAN, Carole S., (1988). Archaeogastropod evolution, phylogeny and systematics: a re-evaluation. *Malacological Review*, Supplement 4, 17-34.

HIGGINS, R. P., (1985). The genus *Echinoderes* (Kinorhyncha: Cyclorhagida) from the English Channel.

HØEG, J. T., (1995). The biology and life cycle of the Rhizocephala (Cirripedia). *Journal of the Marine Biological Association, U.K.*, **75**, 517-550.

HOLDICH, D. M. and JONES, J. A., (1983). *Tanaids*. Synopses of the British Fauna (New Series) No. 27 Cambridge University Press.

HOWARD, C., BRUNTON, C. and CURRY, Gordon B., (1979). *British Brachiopods*. Synopses of the British Fauna (New Series) No. 17 Academic Press. London.

HOWSON, C., (1987). *Directory of the British Marine Fauna and Flora*. Marine Conservation Society, 471pp.

HUSSAIN, N. A. and KNIGHT-JONES, E. W., (1995). Fish and fish-leeches on rocky shores around Britain. *Journal of the Marine Biological Association of the United Kingdom*, **75**, 311-322.

HUYS, Rony and BOXSHALL, Geoffrey, A., (1991). *Copepod Evolution*. Ray Society, London.

HUYS, Rony, BOXSHALL, Geoffrey A. and LINCOLN, Roger J., (1993). The Tantulocaridan Life Cycle: the circle closed? *Journal of Crustacean Biology*, **13**, 432-442.

HUYS, R., GEE, J. M., MOORE, C. G. and HAMOND, R., (1996). *Marine and Brackish Water Harpacticoid Copepods: Part 1*. Synopses of the British Fauna (New Series) No. 51 Field Studies Council, Shrewsbury.

INGLE, R. W., (1980). *British Crabs*. British Museum (Natural History) and Oxford University Press.

INGLE, R. W., (1983). *Shallow-water Crabs*. Synopses of the British Fauna (New Series) No. 25 Cambridge University Press.

INGLE, Ray, (1991). *Larval Stages of Northeastern Atlantic Crabs*. Chapman and Hall.

INGLE, Ray, (1993). *Hermit Crabs of the Northeastern Atlantic Ocean and the Mediterranean Sea*. Chapman and Hall.

INGLE, R. W., (1996). *Shallow-water Crabs*. Synopses of the British Fauna (New Series) No. 25 (2nd Ed.) Field Studies Council, Shrewsbury

INGOLD, M. and RIDDLE, M., (1987). *Hartmann-Shröder's Key to the Polychaete Annelids from the North Sea and Baltic approaches*. Institute of Offshore Engineering, Heriot-Watt University, Edinburgh, 63pp.

ISAAC, M. J., (1975). Copepoda Sub-Order Monstrilloida. *Fiches d'identification du zooplancton*, **144/145**. Conseil International pour l'Exploration de la Mer. Andr. Fred. Høst and Fils, Copenhagen.

IVANOV, A. V., (1963) *Pogonophora*. translated from the Russian by D. B. Carlisle. Academic Press.

JEFFREYS, J. G., (1869). *British Conchology or an account of the Mollusca which now inhabit the British Isles and the surrounding seas*. 5 volumes. Van Vorst, London.

JONES, A. M. and BAXTER, J. M., (1987). *Molluscs: Caudofoveata, Solenogastres, Polyplacophora and Scaphopoda*. Synopses of the British Fauna (New Series) No. 37 E. J. Brill / Dr. W. Backhuys. Leiden.

JONES, N. S., (1976). *British Cumaceans*. Synopses of the British Fauna (New Series) No. 7 Academic Press. London.

JONES-WALTERS, L. M., (1989). Keys to the families of British Spiders. *Field Studies*, 7, 365-443.

JOOSE, Els N. G., (1976). *Littoral Apterygotes (Collembola Thysanura)*. Chapter 7 of CHENG, Lanna, (1976). *Marine Insects*. North Holland / American Elsevier.

KABATA, Z., (1979). *Parasitic Copepoda of British Fishes*. Ray Society, London.

KABATA, Z., (1993). *Copepods parasitic on Fishes*. Synopses of the British Fauna (New Series) No. 47. Universal Book Services / Dr. W. Backhuys. Oegstgeest.

KING, P. E., (1974). *British Sea Spiders*. Synopses of the British Fauna (New Series) No. 5 Academic Press. London.

KING, P. E., (1986). Sea Spiders. A revised key to the adults of littoral Pycnogonida in the British Isles. *Field Studies*, **6**, 493-516.

KIRKPATRICK, P. A. and PUGH, P. R., (1984). *Siphonophores and Velellids*. Synopses of the British Fauna (New Series) No. 29 E. J. Brill / Dr. W. Backhuys. Leiden

KOLBASOV, G. A., (1993). Revision of the genus *Acasta* Leach (Cirripedia: Balanoidea). *Zoological Journal of the Linnean Society*, **109**, 395-427.

KRISTENSEN, R. M., (1983). Loricifera, a new phylum with Aschelminthes characters from the meiobenthos. *Zeitschrift fur Zoologische Systematik und Evolutionsforschung*, **21**: 163-180.

KUKALOVÁ-PECK, Jarmila, (1992). The "Uniramia" do not exist: the ground plan of the Pterygota as revealed by Permian Diaphanopterodea from Russia (Insecta: Palaeodictyopteroidea). *Canadian Journal of Zoology*, **70**, 236-255.

LANG, W. H., (1980). Cirripedia: Balanomorph nauplii of the North Western Atlantic Shores. *Fiches d'identification du zooplancton*, **163**. Conseil International pour l'Exploration de la Mer. Andr. Fred. Høst and Fils, Copenhagen.

LEADER, J. P., (1976). *Marine caddis flies (Trichoptera: Philanisidae)*. Chapter 11 of CHENG, Lanna, (1976). *Marine Insects*. North Holland / American Elsevier.

LEGG, Gerald, and JONES, Richard E., (1988). *Pseudoscorpions*. Synopses of the British Fauna (New Series) No. 40 E. J. Brill / Dr. W. Backhuys. Leiden.

LELOUP, E., (1962). Anthozoa. Ceriantharia: larvae. *Fiches d'identification du zooplancton*, **93**. Conseil International pour l'Exploration de la Mer. Andr. Fred. Høst and Fils, Copenhagen.

LEUNG, Y. -M., (1967). An illustrated key to the whale-lice (Amphipoda, Cyamidae), ectoparasites of Cetacea, with a guide to the literature. *Crustaceana*, **12**(3), 279-291.

LINCOLN, Roger, J., (1979). *British marine Amphipoda: Gammaridea*. British Museum (Natural History) London.

LINCOLN, R. J. and HURLEY, D. E., (1974). Catalogue of the whale-lice (Crustacea: Amphipoda : Cyamidae) in the collection of the British Museum (Natural History). *Bulletin of the British Museum (Zoology)*, **27**(2), 65-72.

LINDBERG, David R., (1988). The Patellogastropoda. *Malacological Review*, Supplement **4**, 17-34.

LLEWELLYN, J., GREEN, J. E. and KEARN, G. C., (1984). A checklist of Monogenean parasites of Plymouth hosts. *Journal of the Marine Biological Association of the United Kingdom*, **64**, 881-887.

LORENZEN, S., 1981. Entwurf eines phylogenetischen Systems der freilebende Nematoden. *Veroeffentlichungen des Instituts fuer Meeresforschung in Bremerhaven* Suppl. 7, 1-472.

LORENZEN, S., 1994. *The Phylogenetic Systematics of Freeliving Nematodes*. Ray Society, London. 383 pp.

MAKINGS, P., (1977). A guide to the British Coastal Mysidacea. *Field Studies*, **4**, 575-595.

MARGULIS, Lynn and SCHWARTZ. Karlene V., (1982; 1988) *Five Kingdoms. An illustrated guide to the phyla of life on Earth*. W. H. Freeman and Company.

MARINE BIOLOGICAL ASSOCIATION, (1957). *Plymouth Marine Fauna*, Third Edition. Marine Biological Association of the United Kingdom, Plymouth.

MANTON, S. M., (1977). *The Arthropoda: Habits, Functional Morphology, and Evolution*. Clarendon. Oxford.

MANUEL, R. L., (1980). *The Anthozoa of the British Isles - a colour guide*. Produced for the Underwater Conservation Society by R. Earll.

MANUEL, R. L., (1988). *British Anthozoa*. Synopses of the British Fauna (New Series) No. 18 (Revised). E. J. Brill / Dr. W. Backhuys. Leiden.

MAUCHLINE, J., (1984). *Euphausiid, Stomatopod and Leptostracan Crustaceans*. Synopses of the British Fauna (New Series) No. 30. E. J. Brill / Dr. W. Backhuys. Leiden.

MCINTYRE, A. D., (1962). The class Kinorhyncha (Echinoderida) in British waters. *Journal of the Marine Biological Association of the United Kingdom*, **42**, 503-509.

MIKKELSEN, P. M. C., (1994). *The evolutionary relationships of Cephalaspidea s.l. (Gastropoda: Opisthobranchia): A phylogenetic analysis*. Unpublished PhD thesis, Florida Institute of Technology, Melbourne.

MILLAR, R. H., (1970). *British Ascidians*. Synopses of the British Fauna (New Series) No. 1 Academic Press, London.

MORGAN, C. I. and KING, P. E., (1976). *British Tardigrades*. Synopses of the British Fauna (New Series) No. 9 Academic Press. London.

MORGAN, C. I. and O'REILLY, M., (1988). Additions to the Scottish Tardigrade Fauna, including a description of *Megastygarctides setelosa* new species, with a revised key for the identification of Scottish marine species. *Glasgow Naturalist*, **21**, 445-454.

MORTON, J. E., (1957). Opisthobranchia order: Gymnosomata. *Fiches d'identification du zooplancton*, **79, 80**. Conseil International pour l'Exploration de la Mer. Andr. Fred. Høst and Fils, Copenhagen.

MOYSE, J., (1987). *Larvae of lepadomorph barnacles*. In SOUTHWARD, A. J. (Ed.) *Barnacle Biology*. Crustacean Issues 5 A. A. Balkema, Rotterdam.

MOYSE, J., (1990). *Cirripedia*. In Chapter 8 of HAYWARD, P. J. and RYLAND, J. S., *The Marine Fauna of the British Isles and North-West Europe*. Clarendon Press, Oxford.

MUUS, B. J., (1963). Cephalopoda. *Fiches d'identification du zooplancton*, **94-98**. Conseil International pour l'Exploration de la Mer. Andr. Fred. Høst and Fils, Copenhagen.

NAYLOR, E., (1972). *British marine Isopods*. Synopses of the British Fauna (New Series) No. 3 Academic Press. London.

NEWELL, G. E., and NEWELL, R. C., (1973). *Marine Plankton A Practical Guide*. Hutchinson. London.

NEWMAN, W. A., (1987). *Evolution of cirripedes and the major groups*. In SOUTHWARD, A. J. (Ed.) *Barnacle Biology*. Crustacean Issues 5 A. A. Balkema, Rotterdam.

OLIVER, P. G., and MEECHAN, C. J., (1993). *Woodlice*. Synopses of the British Fauna (New Series) No. 49. Field Studies Council. Shrewsbury.

PEARSE, Vicki, PEARSE, John, BUCHSBAUM, Mildred and BUCHSBAUM, Ralph, (1987). *Living Invertebrates*. Blackwell Scientific Publications, Boston, Massachusetts.

PICTON, Bernard E., (1985). *Ascidians of the British Isles*. Marine Conservation Society. Ross on Wye.

PICTON, Bernard E., (1993). *A Field Guide to the Shallow-water Echinoderms of the British Isles*. Marine Conservation Society. Immel Publishing.

PIERROT-BULTS, A. C. and CHIDGEY, K. C., (1988). *Chaetognatha*. Synopses of the British Fauna (New Series) No. 39. E. J. Brill / Dr. W. Backhuys. Leiden.

PLATT, H. M. and WARWICK, R. M., (1977). *Free-living Marine Nematodes. Part I. British Enoplids*. Synopses of the British Fauna (New Series) No. 28 Cambridge University Press.

PLATT, H. M. and WARWICK, R. M., (1988). *Free-living Marine Nematodes. Part II. British Chromadorids*. Synopses of the British Fauna (New Series) No. 38 E. J. Brill / Dr. W. Backhuys. Leiden.

PLEIJEL, Fredrik, and DALES, R. P., (1991). *Polychaetes: British Phyllodocoideans, Typhloscolecoideans and Tomopteroideans*. Synopses of the British Fauna (New Series) No. 45. Universal Book Services / Dr. W. Backhuys. Oegstgeest.

POLHEMUS, John T., (1976). *Shore Bugs (Hemiptera: Saldidae etc.)*. Chapter 9 of CHENG, Lanna, (1976). *Marine Insects*. North Holland / American Elsevier.

PONDER, W. F. (Editor), (1988). Prosobranch Phylogeny. Proceedings of a Symposium held at the 9th International Malacological Congress, Edinburgh, 31 August - 6 September, 1986. *Malacological Review*, Supplement **4**.

PONDER, W. F. and WAREN, A., (1988). Appendix. Classification of the Caenogastropoda and Heterostropha - A list of the family-group names and higher taxa. *Malacological Review*, Supplement **4**, 288-312.

POULSEN, Eric M., (1969). Ostracoda I and Ostracoda II - Myodocopa. *Fiches d'identification du zooplancton*, Sheets **115** and **116**. Conseil International pour l'Exploration de la Mer. Andr. Fred. Høst and Fils, Copenhagen.

PRUDHOE, S., (1982). *British Polyclad Turbellarians*. Synopses of the British Fauna (New Series) No. 26. Cambridge University Press.

PRUDHOE, S., (1985). *A monograph on Polyclad Turbellaria*. British Museum (Natural History).

PUGH, P. J. A. and KING, P. E., (1988). Acari of the British supralittoral. *Journal of Natural History*, **22**, 107-122.

RISER, Nathan W., and MORSE, M. Patricia, (1974). *Biology of the Turbellaria*. McGraw Hill.

ROBERTS, Michael J., (1985). *The Spiders of Great Britain and Ireland. Volume 1*. Harley Books, Colchester.

ROTH, Vincent D. and BROWN, Wynne, (1976). *Other Intertidal Air-breathing Arthropods*. Chapter 6 of CHENG, Lanna, (1976). *Marine Insects*. North Holland / American Elsevier.

RUSSELL, F. S., (1953). *The Medusae of the British Isles: Anthomedusae, Leptomedusae, Limnomedusae, Trachymedusae, and Narcomedusae*. Cambridge University Press.

RUSSELL, F. S., (1970). *The Medusae of the British Isles Volume II: Pelagic Scyphozoa, with a supplement to the first volume on Hydromedusae*. Cambridge University Press.

SALVINI-PLAWEN, L. v., (1985). *Early evolution and the primitive groups*. In TRUEMAN, E. R. and CLARK, M. R. *The Mollusca Volume 10: Evolution*. Academic Press.

SAWYER, Roy T., (1986). *Leech Biology and Behaviour*. 3 volumes. Oxford Scientific Publications.

SCHOLTZ, Gerhard, and RICHTER, Stefan, (1995). Phylogenetic systematics of the reptantian Decapoda (Crustacea, Malacostraca). *Zoological Journal of the Linnean Society,* **113,** 289-328.

SCUDDER, Geoffrey G. E., (1976). *Water Boatmen of saline waters (Hemiptera; Corixidae).* Chapter 10 of CHENG, Lanna, (1976). *Marine Insects.* North Holland / American Elsevier.

SHEAR, William A., (1992). End of the 'Uniramia' taxon. *Nature, London.* **359,** 477-478

SHIH, Chant-Tai and DUNBAR, M. J., (1963). Amphipoda Sub-Order: Hyperiidea. Family Phronimidae *Fiches d'identification du zooplancton,* Sheet **104.** Conseil International pour l'Exploration de la Mer. Andr. Fred. Høst and Fils, Copenhagen.

SLUYS, Ronald, (1989). *A monograph of Marine Triclads.* A. A. Balkema. Rotterdam.

SMITH, Shelagh M. and HEPPELL, David (1991) *Checklist of British Marine Mollusca.* National Museums of Scotland

SMALDON, G., (1979). *British Coastal Shrimps and Prawns.* Synopses of the British Fauna (New Series) No. 15 Academic Press. London.

SMALDON, G., HOLTHUIS, L. B. and FRANSEN, C. H. J. M., (1993). *Coastal Shrimps and Prawns.* Synopses of the British Fauna (New Series) No. 15 2nd Edition. Field Studies Council, Shrewsbury.

SMITH, A. B., PATERSON, G. L. J. and LAFAY, B., (1995). Ophiuroid phylogeny and higher taxonomy: morphological, molecular and palaeontological perspectives. *Zoological journal of the Linnean Society,* **114,** 213-243.

SMITH, K. G. V., (1989). An introduction to the immature stages of British flies. *Handbooks for the Identification of British Insects,* **10** part 14. British Museum (Natural History) London.

SOLEM, A., (1978). Classification of Land Molluscs In: FRETTER, V., and PEAKE, J. *Pulmonata Vol.2A: Systematics, Evolution and Ecology.* Academic Press.

SOUTHWARD, A. J. (Ed.), (1987). *Barnacle Biology.* Crustacean Issues 5 A. A. Balkema, Rotterdam.

SOUTHWARD, A. J. and CRISP, D. J., (1963). *Barnacles of European Waters.* Catalogue of main marine fouling organisms Vol. 1 OECD.

SOUTHWARD, Eve C., (1972). *Keys for the identification of Echinodermata of the British Isles.* Marine Biological Association - Echinoderm Survey. Plymouth.

SPOEL, S. van der, (1967). *Euthecosomata.* Bohn, Scheltema and Holkema, Utrecht.

SPOEL, S. van der, (1972). Pteropoda Thecosomata. *Fiches d'identification du zooplancton,* **140-142.** Conseil International pour l'Exploration de la Mer. Andr. Fred. Høst and Fils, Copenhagen.

SPOEL, S. van der, (1976). *Pseudothecosomata, Gymnosomata and Heteropoda (Gastropoda).* Bohn, Scheltema and Holkema, Utrecht.

SPOONER, G. M., (1960). The occurrence of *Ingolfiella* in the Eddystone shell gravel, with description of a new species. *Journal of the Marine Biological Association of the United Kingdom,* **39,** 319-329.

STERRER, Wolfgang and RIEGER, Reinhard, (1974). *Retronectidae - a new cosmopolitan marine family of Catenulida (Turbellaria).* Chapter 4 of RISER, Nathan W. and MORSE, M. Patricia, *Biology of the Turbellaria.* McGraw Hill.

STEPHEN, A. C., (1960). *A synopsis of the Echiuroidea, Sipunculoidea and Priapuloidea of British Waters.* Synopsis of the British Fauna 12. Linnean Society of London.

STEPHEN, A. C., and EDMONDS, S.J., (1972). *The Phyla Sipuncula and Echiura.* British Museum (Natural History) London.

TATTERSALL, W. M. and TATTERSALL, O. S., (1951). *The British Mysidacea.* The Ray Society. London.

TAYLOR, J. D. (ed)., (1996). *Origin and Evolutionary Radiation of the Mollusca.* Oxford Science Publications. 392pp.

TEBBLE, Norman (1966). *British Bivalve Seashells.* British Museum (Natural History) London.

THOMPSON, T. E. (1988). *Molluscs: Benthic Opisthobranchs.* Synopses of the British Fauna (New Series) No. 8 (Second Edition) E. J. Brill / Dr. W. Backhuys.

TIEGS, O. W. and MANTON, S. M., (1958). The evolution of the Arthropoda. *Biological Reviews,* **33,** 255-337.

TILLING, S. M., (1987). A key to the Major Groups of British Terrestrial Invertebrates. *Field Studies,* **6,** 695-766.

TOMLINSON, J. T., (1987). *The burrowing barnacles (Acrothoracica).* In SOUTHWARD, A. J. (Ed.), *Barnacle Biology.* Crustacean Issues 5 A. A. Balkema, Rotterdam.

VAUGHT, Kay Cunningham (1989). *A Classification of the Living Mollusca.* American Malacologists, Inc. Melbourne, Florida. 8

WARWICK, Richard M., PLATT, Howard M. and SOMERFIELD, Paul J. (1997) *Free-living Marine Nematodes Part III, Monhysterids.* Synopses of the British Fauna. No. 53. Field Studies Council, Shrewsbury.

WESTHEIDE, W., (1990). *Polychaetes: Interstitial Families.* Synopses of the British Fauna (New Series) No. 39. Universal Book Services / Dr. W. Backhuys. Oegstgeest.

WILLIAMS, G. C., (1995). Living genera of sea pens (Coelenterata: Octocorallia: Penatulacea): illustrated key and synopsis. *Zoological Journal of the Linnean Society,* **113,** 93-140.

APPENDIX 1

CLASSIFICATION

Phylum	Sub-Phylum	Class	Subclass	Super-Order	Order	Sub-order	Approximate number of British marine species
PLACOZOA							1
PORIFERA		Calcarea					
			Calcinea				
					Clathrinida		1
					Leucettida		1
			Calcaronea				
					Leucosoleniida		3
					Sycettida		7
		Demospongiae					
			Homoscleromorpha				
					Homosclerophorida		3
			Tetractinomorpha				
					Astrophorida		19
					Spirophorida		3
					Lithistida		1
					Hadromerida		29
					Axinellida		37
			Ceractinomorpha				
					Halichondrida		10
					Poecilosclerida		130
					Haplosclerida		30
					Nepheliospongida		1
					Dictyoceratida		3
					Dendroceratida		3
					Verongida		1
CNIDARIA							
	MEDUSOZOA						
		Hydrozoa					
			Leptolida				
					Anthoathecatae		61
					Limnomedusae		
						Limnomedusa	4
					Narcomedusae		

Phylum	Sub-Phylum	Class	Subclass	Super-Order	Order	Sub-order	Approximate number of British marine species
						Narcomedusa	7
					Trachymedusae		
						Trachymedusa	7
					Actinulidae		
						Actinula	
					Leptothecatae		
						Conica	
						Campanulinida	34
						Lafoeida	4
						Haleciida	12
						Plumulariida	51
						Proboscoidea	
						Campanulariida	19
				Siphonophora			55
		Scyphozoa					
					Stauromedusae		7
					Coronatae		7
					Semaeostomae		5
					Rhizostomae		1
	ANTHOZOA						
		Octocorallia					
					Stolonifera		2
					Alcyonacea		3
					Gorgonacea		2
					Pennatulacea		4
		Hexacorallia					
					Ceriantharia		3
					Zoantharia		8
					Actiniaria		45
					Corallimorpharia		1
					Scleractinia		6
CTENOPHORA							
		Tentaculata					
					Cydippida		1
					Lobata		1
		Nuda					
					Beroida		2
PLATYHELMINTHES							
		Turbellaria					
					Acoela		13
					Catenulida		1
					Macrostomatida		5
					Neorhabdocoela		33

Phylum	Sub-Phylum	Class	Subclass	Super-Order	Order	Sub-order	Approximate number of British marine species
					Seriata		6
					Tricladida		6
					Polycladida		19
		Monogenea					39
					Monopisthocotylea		
					Polyopisthocotylea		
		Aspidogastrea					
		Digenea					51
		Cestoda					25
MESOZOA							
		Rhombozoa					
		Orthonectida					
NEMERTEA							
		Anopla					
					Archinemertea		3
					Palaeonemertea		12
					Heteronemertea		26
		Enopla					
					Hoplonemertea		
						Monostilifera	33
						Polystilifera	2
					Bdellonemertea		1
GASTROTRICHA							
					Macrodasyida		14
					Chaetonotida		14
ROTIFERA							
		Seisonidea					1
		Bdelloidea					
					Bdelloida		1
		Monogonata					
					Ploima		30
					Flosculariida		4
					Collothecida		1
KINORHYNCHA							
					Cyclorhagida		10
					Homalorhagida		6
PRIAPULA							
		Priapulida					1
ACANTHOCEPHALA							
NEMATOMORPHA							
					Nectonematida		1

Phylum	Sub-Phylum	Class	Subclass	Super-Order	Order	Sub-order	Approximate number of British marine species
NEMATODA							
			Secernentea				
					Rhabditida		2
					Ascaridida		4
					Spirurida		11
			Adenophorea				
				Enoplia			
					Enoplida		101
				Chromadoria			
					Chromadorida		195
					Monhysterida		93
SIPUNCULA							
			Phascolosomatidea				
					Aspidosiphonida		1
					Phascolosomatida		1
			Sipunculidea				
					Golfingiida		9
					Sipunculida		2
ECHIURA							
					Echiurida		3
					Bonelliida		3
POGONOPHORA							
			Frenulatea				
					Athecanephrida		7
					Thecanephridia		2
ANNELIDA							
			Polychaeta				
					Phyllodocida		214
					Amphinomida		6
					Spintherida		4
					Eunicida		58
					Orbiniida		14
					Spionida		52
					Ctenodrilida		1
					Psammodrilida		2
					Cossurida		1
					Flabelligerida		6
					Sternaspida		1
					Capitellida		36
					Opheliida		16
					Nerillida		16
					Dinophilida		4
					Polygordiida		2

Phylum	Sub-Phylum	Class	Subclass	Super-Order	Order	Sub-order	Approximate number of British marine species
					Protodrilida		13
					Oweniida		2
					Terebellida		48
					Sabellida		43
		Myzostomata					
					Myzostomida		1
		Clitellata					
			Oligochaeta				
					Haplotaxida		
					Tubificina		71
			Hirudinoida				
					Rhynchobdellida		22
MOLLUSCA							
		Caudofoveata					
					Chaetodermatida		3
		Solenogastres					
					Pholidoskepia		5
					Neomeniamorpha		2
					Cavibelonia		4
		Polyplacophora					
			Neoloricata				
					Lepidopleurina		8
					Ischnochitonina		6
					Acanthochitonina		2
		Gastropoda					
			Prosobranchia				
				Patellogastropoda			9
				Archaeogastropoda			
					Vetigastropoda		37
					Cocculiniformia		1
				Caenogastropoda			
					Neotaenioglossa		145
					Neogastropoda		49
			Heterobranchia				
					Heterostropha		61
			Euthyneura				
				Opisthobranchia			
					Cephalaspidea		27
					Acochlidioidea		8
					Sacoglossa		10
					Anaspidea		5
					Notaspidea		4
					Thecosomata		19

Phylum	Sub-Phylum	Class	Subclass	Super-Order	Order	Sub-order	Approximate number of British marine species
					Gymnosomata		21
					Nudibranchia		121
			Pulmonata				
					Systelommatophora		1
					Archaeopulmonata		3
		Scaphopoda					
					Dentalioidea		2
					Siphonodentalioidea		2
		Bivalvia					
			Protobranchia				
					Nuculoida		13
			Lamellibranchia				
					Arcoida		5
					Mytiloida		15
					Pterioida		2
					Limoida		7
					Ostreoida		22
					Veneroida		122
					Myoida		2
					Pholadomyoida		9
			Septibranchia				
					Poromyoida		8
		Cephalopoda					
					Sepioida		18
					Teuthoida		21
					Octopoda		6
PHORONA							3
BRACHIOPODA							
		Inarticulata					
					Acrotretida		2
		Articulata					
					Rhynchonellida		3
					Terebratulida		16
BRYOZOA							
		Stenolaemata					
					Cyclostomatida		36
		Gymnolaemata					
					Ctenostomatida		45
					Cheilostomatida		219
ENTOPROCTA							
					Solitaria		15
					Coloniales		7

Phylum	Sub-Phylum	Class	Subclass	Super-Order	Order	Sub-order	Approximate number of British marine species
CYCLIOPHORA							
		Eucycliophora					
					Symbiida		1
ARTHROPODA							
	CRUSTACEA						
		Branchiopoda					
					Cladocera		6
		Tantulocarida					1
		Cirripedia					
					Thoracica		
						Pedunculata	9
						Sessilia	13
					Acrothoracica		
						Apygophora	1
					Rhizocephala		
						Kentrogonida	19
						Akentrogonida	4
		Ostracoda					
					Myodocopida		86
					Platycopida		2
					Podocopida		116
		Copepoda					
					Platycopioida		1
					Calanoida		24
					Misophrioida		1
					Cyclopoida		57
					Mormonilloida		2
					Harpacticoida		800
					Poecilostomatoida		107
					Siphonostomatoida		161
					Monstrilloida		26
		Malacostraca					
			Phyllocarida				
					Leptostraca		7
			Holpocarida				
					Stomatopoda		2
			Peracarida				
					Mysidacea		74
					Cumacea		41
					Tanaidacea		27
					Isopoda		85
					Amphipoda		
						Gammaridea	269

Phylum	Sub-Phylum	Class	Subclass	Super-Order	Order	Sub-order	Approximate number of British marine species
						Hyperiidea	8
						Ingolfiellidea	1
						Caprellidea	14
				Eucarida			
					Euphausiacea		16
					Decapoda		154
CHELICERATA							
		Arachnida					
					Aranea		1
					Pseudoscorpiones		1
					Acariformes		
						Mesostigmata	36
						Prostigmata	74
						Cryptostigmata	28
						Astigmata	4
	ATELOCERATA						
		Pauropoda					4
		Diplopoda					
					Julida		1
		Chilopoda					
					Geophilida		3
		Hexapoda					
			Collembola				
					Arthroploena		18
			Apterygota				
					Archaeognatha		4
			Pterygota				
					Anoplura		1
					Hemiptera		2
					Trichoptera		1
					Coleoptera		10
					Diptera		46
PYCNOGONIDA							30
LOBOPODIA							
		TARDIGRADA					
			Heterotardigrada				
					Arthrotardigrada		11
			Eutardigrada				5
CHAETOGNATHA							
HEMICHORDATA							
		Enteropneusta					9
		Pterobranchia					
					Rhabdopleurida		2

Phylum	Sub-Phylum	Class	Subclass	Super-Order	Order	Sub-order	Approximate number of British marine species
ECHINODERMATA							
		Crinoidea					
					Comatulida		3
		Asteroidea					
					Phanerozonida		5
					Spinulosida		8
					Forcipulatida		4
		Ophiuroidea					
					Euryalae		2
					Ophiurae		14
		Echinoidea					
					Diadematoida		5
					Clypeastroida		1
					Spatangoida		5
		Holothuroidea					
					Aspidochirotida		2
					Dendrochirotida		12
					Apodida		5
CHORDATA							
	UROCHORDATA						
		Ascidiacea					
					Aplousobranchia		22
					Phlebobranchia		12
					Pleurogona		26
		Thaliacea					
					Pyrosomida		2
					Doliolida		3
					Salpida		12
		Larvacea					
					Copelata		4
CEPHALOCHORDATA							
					Amphioxida		1

Total 5775

INDEX

The AIDGAP Publications

The following AIDGAP titles have been published by the Field Studies Council

A key to the adults of British lacewings and their allies Colin Plant (1997)

A key to the major groups of marine invertebrates John Crothers (1997)

A field key to the shore fishes of the British Isles Alwyne Wheeler (1994)

Random-access identification guides for a microcomputer (includes a sedges database) Available in BBC and IBM formats, Colin Legg (1992)

The Fern Guide: an introductory guide to the ferns, clubmosses, quillworts and horsetails of the British Isles James Merryweather & Michael Hill (1992)

A field guide to the sharks of British coastal waters Philip Vas (1991)

A key to the woodlice of Britain and Ireland Stephen Hopkin (1991)

Insects of the British cow-dung community Peter Skidmore (1991)

British Sawflies (Hymenoptera: Symphyta): a key to adults of the genera occurring in Britain Adam Wright (1990)

Soil Types: a field identification guide Stephen Trudgill (1989)

Keys to the families of British Spiders Lawrence Jones-Walters (1989)

A key to adults of British Water Beetles L.E. Friday (1988)

A key to the major groups of British Terrestrial Invertebrates S.M. Tilling (1987)

A key to the major groups of British Freshwater Invertebrates P.S. Croft (1986)

Sea Spiders. A revised key to the adults of littoral Pycnogonida in the British Isles Phil King (1986)

A field guide to the British Red Seaweeds (Rhodophyta) Sue Hiscock (l986)

British Grasses, a punched-card key to Grasses in the vegetative state Richard Pankhurst & Judith Allinson (1985)

Bees, Ants & Wasps – the British Aculeates Pat Willmer (1985)

A key to the families of British Coleoptera (beetles) and Strepsiptera Dennis Unwin (1984: revised 1988)

A field guide to the Slugs of the British Isles R.A.D. Cameron, B. Eversham & N. Jackson (1983) OUT OF PRINT

A key to the Crabs and Crab-like Animals of British inshore waters John & Marilyn Crothers (1983: revised 1988)

A key to families of British Diptera Dennis Unwin (1981)

An illustrated guide to the Diatoms of British coastal plankton J.B. Sykes (1981)

A Field key to the British Brown Seaweeds Sue Hiscock (1979) OUT OF PRINT

These, and many other FSC titles, may be purchased when visiting Field Studies Council Centres or may be ordered through the post from:
FSC Publications, Field Studies Council, Preston Montford, Shrewsbury SY4 1HW
Tel: 01743 850370 • Fax: 01743 850178

A complete list of titles and prices is also available from this address.